"Why Have You Come?"

His face was hard. "I told you. I thought we should discuss the : . . uh, arrangements."

She frowned. "Arrangements?"

He hunched his shoulders irritably. "Yes. I don't intend to displace you or the members of your family, but I do have to have someplace to live, and I have a legal right to use Fox Briar."

She stared for a moment, then realized his intentions. "Are you saying that you actually intend to move into this house? That we are going to have to live together?"

He smiled, baring his teeth so that she thought of a stalking tiger.

"Live together?" he repeated, as though trying out the words. "That does have a nice ring to it. . . ."

KAREN YOUNG
and her husband, Paul, have moved eighteen times during twenty-five years of marriage. Because of their mobile life-style, Karen has observed many different types of people and has included them in her plots.

Dear Reader:

I'd like to take this opportunity to thank you for all your support and encouragement of Silhouette Romances.

Many of you write in regularly, telling us what you like best about Silhouette, which authors are your favorites. This is a tremendous help to us as we strive to publish the best contemporary romances possible.

All the romances from Silhouette Books are for you, so enjoy this book and the many stories to come.

Karen Solem
Editor-in-Chief
Silhouette Books

KAREN YOUNG
Irresistible Intruder

Silhouette *Romance*

Published by Silhouette Books New York

America's Publisher of Contemporary Romance

Silhouette Books by Karen Young

Yesterday's Promise (ROM #212)
Irresistible Intruder (ROM #284)

 SILHOUETTE BOOKS, a Division of Simon & Schuster, Inc.
1230 Avenue of the Americas, New York, N.Y. 10020

Copyright © 1984 by Karen Young

Distributed by Pocket Books

ISBN: 0-671-57284-9

First Silhouette Books printing March, 1984

10 9 8 7 6 5 4 3 2 1

All of the characters in this book are fictitious. Any resemblance to actual persons, living or dead, is purely coincidental.

Map by Ray Lundgren

To my husband, Paul

Irresistible
Intruder

SOUTHERN
MISSISSIPPI

Places in *italics* are fictitious.

Chapter One

"Watch it, Mark!" Ben Scott's involuntary cry sounded above the screech of brakes as the sleek Mercedes swerved to avoid a slightly unsteady figure that had materialized out of the thick fog that blanketed the streets in an almost impenetrable mist. There was a trace of pale light, but visibility was practically nonexistent.

"That fool almost made a hood ornament for my car," Mark Devereaux growled, thrusting the door open and stepping out to peer into the hazy evening. "I think we're at the hotel, but I can't find the entrance to the car park. It'll be a damned nuisance if we have to cruise the French Quarter looking for a parking place."

He left the door ajar and walked a few steps toward a glow of lights that hopefully marked the drive, and Kate Langford noticed, not for the first time, that Mark appeared a bit unsteady himself.

Since it was the Mardi Gras season, he had probably had a few drinks before coming to her room to pick her up. At the time, she had been preoccupied with her own thoughts and had failed to react in her customary fashion, which would have been a flat refusal to honor her commitment or to demand to drive herself. She had done neither, and now a tiny frown puckered her forehead delicately, and she sighed impatiently. Mark was going to be a problem before the night was over. She could feel it, and she dreaded it. She was in no mood to cater to his ego, and experience had taught her that when he was drunk, he became more than ordinarily possessive.

Ben's voice interrupted her thoughts. "Well, I'm glad we're here and in one piece," he declared thankfully, his eyes following Mark's outline, already disappearing in the mist. "Mark's driving had me unstrung for a minute. I expected to wind up in a ditch."

His wife laughed. "You must have been worried. You squeezed my arm as we turned that last corner, and I've got the bruises to prove it." She rubbed her wrist ruefully.

"Oh, Charlotte! I'm really sorry." Kate began an apology. "I didn't know Mark was in no condition to drive."

Charlotte smiled, reaching over the seat and patting Kate's shoulder. "Forget it. You're not responsible for Mark's behavior."

"Right," Ben agreed. "If it hadn't been only a few blocks, I would have refused to continue, but I misjudged his condition, I'm afraid."

Kate leaned back against the car's luxurious upholstery, but it was impossible to relax. She chewed her lower lip fretfully, wishing she were elsewhere that night. She would hardly be lighthearted company for her escort or her friends, but it had been difficult to manufacture a plausible excuse to decline, since she had already made the trip to New Orleans. After all, it was a festive season. Mardi Gras was a time of almost insane revelry, and the mood of the crowd would probably prove contagious. She should try to make the most of it, now that she was committed.

Mark's hand appeared on the frame of the door, and he sank heavily into the seat. "The entrance is just a few feet in front of us if these idiots will stay clear for a minute and let me through." He slammed the door with unnecessary force and started the car.

"Mark, I don't think . . ." Kate's uncertain words faded as Mark turned to face her.

"Look, baby, let's not waste time thinking to-night. We're here for a party, and the sooner we get inside, the sooner we can begin. Okay?" And without waiting for any reply, he guided the car through the entrance and whipped into the first available slot.

There was a collective sigh of relief as his passengers got out of the car, and Kate angrily gathered up her bag and stole. She couldn't remember why she had ever agreed to Mark's suggestion that they attend the ball together. Lately, she had become aware of qualities in him that she had never noticed before. There was a streak of thoughtlessness in him, but since she had known him for years, she supposed familiarity had rendered her strangely unobservant. There were other things, too, but her old inclination to overlook them seemed in danger of disappearing. If she had been unsure whether she wanted to continue seeing Mark, then the evening seemed to be crystallizing her vague dissatisfaction into certainty. Distasteful as it would be, there would have to be some plain speaking between them, and soon.

Her face was flushed, and her chin tilted danger-ously as they surged forward with the crowd. Mark presented the engraved invitation to an attendant, who gave it a careful scrutiny and then granted them entrance to one of the most elaborate and prestigious of New Orleans's impressive Mardi Gras spectacles—the Bacchus Ball.

Traditionally held on the Sunday night before "Fat Tuesday," the actual Mardi Gras day, the Bacchus Krewe, which rolled at night, had the distinction of being a major parade. The resulting carnival atmosphere, which began with the parade and continued on into the evening, culminating in the fabulous ball, was an impressive, colorful affair with participants costumed, masked and generally incognito. With their identity concealed, even the most repressed personalities often behaved with an incredible lack of circumspection, to put it mildly.

Kate eyed the merrymakers with a slight sense of unreality mixed with a resignation that had no place in the carnival atmosphere. Even though she had been exposed from childhood to the Mardi Gras, which ended at midnight on Shrove Tuesday and was marked by the beginning of the Lenten season on Ash Wednesday, she still felt overwhelmed by the uninhibited actions displayed by the thousands of people who thronged the narrow streets of New Orleans's French Quarter to celebrate. Although her friends often characterized Kate as willful and sophisticated, there was a core of reserve in her that was deeply ingrained. Kate was never more aware of that slight reserve in herself than at Mardi Gras.

Thankfully, she did not have to don a ridiculous costume. She and Mark had agreed to wear only the traditional black mask, and a quick, comprehensive look around showed her they were not alone. Many people had chosen evening clothes instead of an elaborate costume, but still the crowd was alive with colorful and eccentric outfits.

She glanced worriedly at Mark, chewing thoughtfully on her lower lip as she watched him down yet another stiff whisky and water. She hoped the amount of water was substantial enough to ward off a state of complete inebriation, but she suspected it was already too late. His face was flushed, and he was laughing too loudly. Again, she wished fervently that she was back at Fox Briar in her own room with the windows opened and the sound of the Gulf gently monotonous in her ears instead of the raucous sounds that amplified the throbbing in her head. She reached up and pulled the mask off, hoping to relieve some of the discomfort.

"Come on, Kate," Mark wheedled. "We're supposed to be having a ball! Get it?"

"A very bad pun, Mark," Ben commented dryly. "How about slowing down on the booze. We've got a long night ahead."

Mark frowned with heavy concentration. "I'm in great shape, Ben, ol' buddy. Don't you worry 'bout me."

Kate clicked her tongue disgustedly, looking away from the sight of Mark's drunkenness, trying to remember that he was really not too bad when he wasn't drinking and wondering at the same time once again why she had agreed to come that night. Her eyes wandered over the crowd, and she felt a slight prickly sensation. Was someone watching her? She tried to find the source of the eerie feeling, but no one seemed to be particularly suspicious. With a shrug of her shoulders, she told herself it was just the night and her own sense of not belonging. When Mark tugged at her hand to pull her out on the dance floor, she reluctantly allowed it. Maybe getting him away from the bar would slow down the inevitable, she thought with scant hope.

"Hmm, this is nice," he whispered in her ear, nuzzling the skin under her mane of sun-streaked hair. "You smell good, too."

She pulled away fractionally, hesitant to make a scene but utterly repelled by Mark's condition and his attempts to make love on the dance floor. He pulled her even closer against him, and since she had allowed his advances during the past few months when they had dated frequently, she didn't struggle to free herself. She simply suffered his embrace, telling herself the music would soon end and she could escape to their table where she would announce that she had had enough for one evening. She had no doubt Ben and Charlotte would understand.

"Come on, honey, loosen up." Mark's hands were heavy on her waist and Kate began to resist. Enough was enough. Mark's hold tightened. "You were ready and willing last night," he accused in a carrying voice, and Kate looked around in dismay, hoping no one was paying any attention to their tense struggle and Mark's totally misleading words.

She blinked as she encountered a cold, contemptuous glance from a tall, lean man. The lighting on the dance floor was dim, but his powerful outline, clad in traditional black evening clothes, emphasized the latent masculinity beneath the formal attire. He stood out even in a crowd of similarly clad men, and Kate felt a tiny prickle along the back of her neck. She looked again, telling herself that lots of men had that same lithe, powerful physique. He was masked, but in the indistinct light, the shape of his face, that firmly chiseled jaw, could easily—She caught herself up sharply. This was ridiculous. The man was dancing circumspectly with a fabulous-looking blonde, smiling into her eyes. Kate could see his head bend attentively, and she wondered how he could look so coldly into her eyes one minute and then smile so warmly into those of the woman with whom he was dancing.

Her chin lifted. Who did he think he was? Did he

believe for a minute that she welcomed the obnoxious treatment that Mark was dishing out? She glared back at him, her own eyes flashing defiantly. Instead of sympathetic understanding while she strained to escape Mark's heavy-handed pawing, her accuser merely pronounced judgment. And it was a harsh judgment, Kate was certain as she jerked violently free of Mark's embrace, no longer caring whether she made a scene or not. She cast another stern glance into the masked features of the stranger and headed back to the table.

Ben and Charlotte looked up questioningly as she appeared and took her seat, restrained fury in every line of her quivering body.

"What's wrong?" Charlotte asked, eying the jerky movements Kate made as she collected her bag and the glinting gold knitted shawl that she had draped over the back of her chair.

"Mark is too far gone to make it through the evening," Kate began in a tight voice, as much from the unsettling encounter with the accusing stranger as from the natural anger she felt with Mark for his irresponsible drinking. "I'm going to go back to the hotel, since I can see the evening will only get worse."

"Oh, do you have to go, Kate?" Dismay colored Charlotte's voice, and she appealed to her husband. "Can't you do something, Ben?"

Ben shook his head. "I'm afraid not, honey. Mark must have had a good head start on the sauce before he ever appeared tonight. It's probably best if Kate does leave now." He started to rise, but Kate forestalled him.

"Don't get up, Ben. I'm perfectly capable of calling a taxi, and besides"—she flashed her beautiful smile—"I don't want to ruin the evening for you two. I know you've looked forward to the Bacchus Ball, and I don't want you to miss it on my account."

"I would be happy to take you back, Kate." Ben still looked doubtful.

"Thanks, but I can manage." She felt a hand on her arm and turned to find Mark at her side.

"You're leaving, aren't you?" He swayed slightly as he directed an appealing look into her eyes.

Kate's irritation faded slightly. After all, Mark was a long-time friend, and when he wasn't half bombed, he was good company. "Yes, I am, Mark. Would you like to go with me?"

He took a deep breath, still unsteady on his feet. "Yes. I brought you here, and I can take you back to the hotel," he said, enunciating carefully.

Ben began a protest, but Kate interrupted. "Don't worry, Ben. I plan to drive, and since we're both staying at the same hotel, there won't be any problem. I'll see you both in the morning for breakfast." She swept the stole over one shoulder, and pretending to use Mark's arm as a support, she actually guided him through the mad throng and out of the entrance where she ordered his car with a confidence that made the attendant react swiftly.

While she waited, she peered into the still-thick fog, shrugging aside any momentary doubt about venturing into the night when visibility was so poor. Lights were still blurred and shapes indistinct as she surveyed the street, swarming with revelers oblivious to the nasty weather. Mark's condition and her own lack of enthusiasm for the evening combined to harden her resolve, and she squared her shoulders determinedly. Mark's restlessness barely registered as she considered the simplest and most expedient route through the haze.

"I'm driving, Kate," Mark announced, the words coming out slightly slurred.

"We'll see." She stood stiffly, her slim foot tapping, impatience in the taut line of her mouth and her clenched teeth. If the attendant would only hurry, she might get Mark in the car and on the passenger side without too much trouble. The longer he had to argue, the more determined he would become. Once again, that strange prickling sensation feathered along her nerves, and she knew that someone was staring at her again. But the Mercedes was being brought up with a flourish by the young attendant, obviously enjoying the sleek machine, and she was immediately occupied in persuading Mark into the car.

It was hopeless. The more she cajoled, the more sulky and obstinate he became. "Mark," she said with determined patience, "even you must admit you're in no condition to drive."

"I brought you here, and I'm taking you back," he repeated stubbornly for the fifteenth time. He reached for her arm and grasped it in a surprisingly strong grip. He was thrusting her into the car when a voice sliced with cold precision into their tense struggle.

"I believe the lady would prefer to drive."

Kate turned wide, disbelieving eyes toward the source of that voice. Those strange prickles of premonition had not been wrong. It was the same man who had witnessed her humiliating struggle on the dance floor, whose scathing assessment of her had succeeded in crystallizing her decision to leave. She closed her mouth with a snap of her teeth. It was too good to be true that she should escape that night before this final humiliation, she thought darkly.

"Who the hell are you?" Mark demanded.

Totally ignoring Mark, the stranger turned to Kate, his face revealing only the firm-lipped line of his mouth and the unmistakable sherry-brown eyes that were indelibly impressed on her memory. A clear sherry brown like broken glass, the color warm and compelling or cold and hard, depending on his mood. She sucked her breath in sharply, her mind skittering off that memory.

She looked into those eyes now and found that somehow he was not ridiculous behind the black mask of Mardi Gras. No, never ridiculous. Chase would always look right, have everything under control, no matter what the situation. She blinked to try and concentrate on what he was saying.

"I suggest that you find an alternative to driving home with him." Only a flick of his lashes was wasted on Mark's hotly aggressive face.

"Now, look here . . . " Mark moved from the open door, and when he did, Chase turned to face him squarely. Kate could sense Mark's hesitancy. Only a hard, implacable look was necessary to quell the blustery threat, which died before it was born.

Kate was suddenly galvanized into action. "I am perfectly capable of—"

The look he turned on her held no vestige of recognition, and her self-confidence faltered slight ly. She was torn between an incredible impulse to allow Chase the masterful handling of an awkward situation, which she knew he was more than capable of, and rigidly maintaining her right to manage her own affairs independently. She cast away the fleeting inclination to accept anything from him. It had been too long since she had needed Chase Jamison.

"I'm perfectly capable of managing Mark," she stated categorically.

For the first time, humor lit the depths of his eyes, warming them infinitesimally. "How tactless of you to say so," he remarked, raising a sardonic brow above the mask. "Don't you know you are supposed to handle a drunk with kid gloves? If you get his back up, he'll never let you have your way."

Kate stared into his eyes, ignoring the angry sputtering that Chase's words drew from Mark.

Behind the mask, his features were obscured, and doubt assailed her momentarily. Didn't he recognize her? Surely he recognized her even though it had been—what? Eight years? She couldn't have changed that much.

His face swam back into focus, and she forgot suddenly the predicament she was in, aware only of lean features shielded behind the black mask and the compelling, vigorous masculinity beneath the austere evening clothes. Quickly, she shook her head, the weight of her tawny hair swinging against her face. It was only her fanciful imagination, she assured herself, although she had not been subject to the caprices of her troublesome mind for a long time.

"Kate!" Her thoughts were brought up short by Mark's peevish call.

She wrenched her eyes from the magnetic gaze and vaguely turned to Mark. "I'm driving, Mark. Move over."

He opened his mouth to protest.

"You heard her. If you want to stay in the car, use the passenger's side. If you don't, then I'll take the lady home."

Swept along by a sense of events out of her control, Kate watched while Mark responded to the note of authority and hitched himself over the gear shift, settling into the right side with a sulky look. Kate then seated herself behind the wheel, turning to express her thanks when Mark's voice came from beside her.

"Have it your way. The sooner we're back at the hotel, the better," he said suggestively, and Kate watched with dismay as the warmth that had lingered in Chase's eyes faded to a cold censure that chilled her as comprehension dawned on him. Kate felt her temper begin to rise again. He thought she and Mark were staying together at the hotel, and he

was again presuming to judge her. She gritted her
teeth, and a spark entered her eyes, turning them a
deep midnight blue. She started the car with a
savage twist of the key, ignoring the rigid disapprov-
al in his cold regard and turning away to afford him
the cool, averted lines of her perfect profile. Let him
think what he pleases, she thought angrily.

"I'll be seeing you, Kate," he said, and then,
incredibly, he added, "I'm coming home."

Kate gasped, swinging around with wide eyes, but
his expression was withdrawn, the line of his chin
firm beneath the ludicrous mask.

She opened her mouth, but no words came.

His gaze raked over her to Mark, and his mouth
thinned contemptuously. Then he straightened away
from the car almost as if he would give them both a
helping shove out of his sight.

Now all doubt was removed. It seemed incredible
to Kate that there should have been even a moment
when Chase's identity was doubtful, considering the
impact he had made on her life. But that had been a
long time ago, she told herself.

With shaking hands, she put the car in gear and
drove away, gaining speed as fast as she dared,
firmly resisting the impulse to catch a last glimpse of
him in the mirror. The mist seemed to be lifting
slightly, thank heavens, and she concentrated on
threading her way through the crowded streets.
Escape was uppermost in her mind, and she drove as
though the devil himself was just over her shoulder.

Later that evening, she undressed with a flat,
let-down feeling, slipping out of the flowing cream
crepe and dropping it carelessly on a chair. Mechanically, she removed her bra and pantyhose, drawing
up before the wide hotel mirror. A slim, elegantly
feminine grace characterized her movements. Seeking to relieve the tension that tightened the cords in
her neck, she slipped both hands under the dark gold

weight of her hair, lifting it in an unconsciously seductive gesture, rotating her head around to try and relax. She stared into the mirror. As though meeting her own gaze straight on conjured up more than she bargained for, her glance bounced away, a tiny frown appearing between expressive brows.

She wanted to push chaotic and unsettling thoughts out of her mind, and she wished again that she was at home. An image of Fox Briar floated across her mind, its Old South elegance faded but still possessing a charm that captivated. Kate had lived all her life in the sixty-year-old house situated on a pine- and oak-studded portion of land on the Gulf Coast in Mississippi. Despite its faded grandeur, to Kate it had always been peaceful and nurturing, the timelessness striking a chord within her. For Fox Briar, age had simply enhanced its appeal. She looked up into her own reflection again. Would Chase think the years had enhanced her?

Coolly she inspected her mirror image, tilting her tawny head slightly. She was no longer the uninhibited seventeen-year-old whose precocious personality had delighted and dismayed her doting grandmother and indulgent father. That girl had disappeared eight years earlier, to be replaced with the cool-eyed beauty whose indigo-blue gaze effectively masked the seething emotions that the chance encounter that evening had awakened.

She moved impatiently, willing her mind to concentrate on something else. What an unsatisfying evening! Mark's behavior once they got away from the ball had been the final straw that finished off her fragile composure. She had delivered him to his hotel-room door and ordinarily would have found his bewildered surprise amusing when it dawned on him that, for Kate, the evening was over. No amount of persuasive charm—and Mark had more than his share—could crack her firm refusal to enter his room for a nightcap, as she knew from experience, what would follow the drink.

Poor Mark. He couldn't possibly know that she was hardly aware of him, so distracted was she by meeting Chase again. The aura of sheer animal magnetism that surrounded him was as compelling as it ever had been. She frowned suddenly. She had consciously avoided thinking about the one man she could never forget, but his image wouldn't go away, and neither would the sensual heat that invaded her veins when she thought of Chase.

What would she do if he came back to town? Had his statement been made for some devious purpose of his own? Or had he just wanted to shock her, to try and catch her unaware? Her mouth twisted bitterly. He was good at that. He had always managed to make her feel at a disadvantage, she thought, recalling the rush of emotion that swept her as their eyes met that night. Although the cold features beneath the black mask had not revealed a vestige of recognition, she had known it was Chase. When outside in the mist-shrouded evening she was trying to reason with Mark, she had experienced the same foolish inclination to let Chase take charge, to place herself in those lean, capable hands. Her mind's eye recalled them vividly. Tanned, strong, sensual.

Still, the training of years had taught her to resist the pull of past fantasies. That was all it was, she told herself. A foolish fantasy from her past.

Knowing the value of action, she walked quickly to the bathroom and turned on the shower. She shed her filmy underwear, stepping quickly under the water. She lifted her face, hoping that the pelting spray would wash away the traces of her makeup and the wayward trend of her thoughts as well, but it was a useless hope, as the image of Chase kept returning like a homing pigeon.

Why was he coming back? she mused, draping a large towel around her body and moving into the bedroom. She frowned and shook the damply curling weight of her hair restlessly, some deep-seated instinct stirring inside her. It would be fatal to allow Chase's image to grow and strengthen in her mind. Although she was certainly not naive where men were concerned, no other man had ever been capable of inciting her emotions the way Chase did.

She flung the towel aside and reached for a peach satin gown, dropping it quickly over her heated body. Grabbing a hairbrush she began stroking the sun-heightened strands of her hair.

Ironically, Chase's last impression had been a completely false one. She had never slept with Mark, but from the contempt on Chase's face, he would never believe that. He would think the worst of her. That look on his face had been familiar. Just as he had looked that night . . .

The vigorous movement of the hairbrush faltered, and Kate swallowed a little sigh of regret, reminding herself that he had a lot of nerve judging her from appearances. He could hardly afford the luxury of criticizing her, considering the fact that he was guilty of treachery and betrayal. Not to mention how cruel he had been to her personally.

She laid the hairbrush aside and snapped off the light, plunging the room into gloom. Still unsettled, she wandered to the balconied French doors, opening one and slipping outside. The air was cooler, and the mist was almost completely dissipated, she noted with relief, thinking of the drive home the next day.

With no light behind her, she was able to look down into the teeming crowd below without reserve, wondering at the crazy antics of the Mardi Gras revelers. A tiny smile hovered on her mouth, and her eyes strayed upward. A full moon, she noted without surprise. Her smile deepened, recalling stories of weird behavior when the moon was in its full phase. She twitched her shoulders, feeling her sense of humor returning. That probably accounted for the extraordinary path that her own thoughts had taken, she mused, mentally resolving to avoid Mardi Gras and a full moon in the future.

She turned and stepped back inside her room, moving to the bed and slipping between the cool sheets. She settled down, moving a little to find a comfortable position. She yawned sleepily.

Chase Jamison couldn't affect her anymore. She was now immune to that aggressive male type, she told herself. But he was certainly an attractive man, even more so after eight years. . . .

Chapter Two

The gray green of February was all around as Kate's gaze surveyed the familiar landscape from the car window. Ben and Charlotte Scott occupied the front seat, their desultory conversation drifting unnoticed, while Kate's thoughts wavered between the events of the night before and a slightly wary caution when she thought of events to come.

Morning had brought about a firm, new resolve. It was silly of her to allow something that had happened eight years earlier to shake her present confidence. After all, even if Chase returned to Baytown, the chances were practically nil that they would meet. And no matter how she racked her brain, she couldn't think of an explanation for his return. Whatever it was, it had nothing to do with her, and the niggling little fear that wouldn't quite be banished was a normal reaction to Chase's sudden reappearance when she hadn't thought of him in years. Or so she told herself.

The car moved swiftly through Louisiana, Interstate 10 flanked on both sides by characteristic swampland hosting thick subtropical growth of palmetto and bald cypress. Soon the marsh-loving vegetation would give way to the vivid green, even in winter, of pine and live oak as well as the darkly beautiful foliage of Mississippi's beloved magnolia.

"You know," Charlotte began pensively, "this year Mardi Gras just wasn't as much fun as it usually is. I couldn't wait for the season to begin, but now I'm thinking maybe we should skip it next year. There are people who say you should only "do" Mardi Gras every five years."

"There's no maybe about it for me," Kate said emphatically. "I really shouldn't have come this year. I had mixed feelings about it in the first place, but Mark's mother has that party every year, and she would never accept a refusal no matter how ingenuous an excuse I could have thought up."

"Look at it this way, girls." Ben spoke up without taking his eye off the road. "We had four days' vacation away from work, and all of it wasn't that bad."

Charlotte grimaced. "That's easy for you to say, but last night Mark was really too much. Kate's evening was over almost before it began."

"Yeah, that was too bad, Kate." He was silent a moment while overtaking a slow-moving farm vehicle. "He didn't give you any trouble back at the hotel, did he?"

Kate smiled, acknowledging Ben's concern for her. "Not really. Mark is a very good-natured drunk. We parted at his door, and I'll bet he doesn't remember anything from two minutes after that. You must have noticed at breakfast this morning how terribly apologetic he was."

Charlotte wasn't quite so understanding. "He

really is the limit, Kate. Why you keep on seeing him is beyond me. You could have any of a dozen men with just a crook of your little finger, but nobody holds your interest for more than a few weeks."

"Mind your own business, honey," Ben said mildly, reaching over and tugging one of his wife's black curls.

Kate leaned back, a faint smile playing across her lips. Charlotte would like nothing better than to see Kate married. They had been roommates in college and were still the best of friends. It was one of those lucky coincidences that Charlotte had married Ben Scott. Ben was employed by Langford Marine, the shipyard owned by Kate's family. Kate herself worked there, functioning in a general capacity, her position titled innocuously administrative assistant, though it surprised no one who knew her father, Phillip Langford.

Kate loved her father dearly, but his doting, dreaming personality certainly wasn't suited for the keen competition needed in the modern shipbuilding industry. Between them, she and Ben Scott had over the past three years bridged the gaps in Phillip's management of Langford Marine. Therefore, her relationship with the Scotts was forged by affection as well as friendship and mutual respect.

"Did I thank you both for inviting me to drive to New Orleans with you?" There was genuine appreciation in Kate's voice. "It would have been a dull trip by myself."

"Forget it," Charlotte replied. "Since we both had the same invitations, it was ridiculous for you to drive alone."

As Ben and Mark Devereaux had grown up together in a small town just north of New Orleans, Ben and Charlotte received invitations to Ben's mother's, Carrie Devereaux's, annual Mardi Gras party. Cypress Pointe, Mark's home, was some distance from the city, and Ben and Charlotte had chosen to stay in a hotel downtown in the heart of the French Quarter. When Kate announced her intention to do the same, Mark had immediately forsaken Cypress Pointe and booked a room next door. The four days had passed quickly, but Kate was more than ready to go home.

Charlotte exaggerated slightly when she accused Kate of tiring of most of the men who were attracted to her within a few weeks. But for the most part, she didn't seem to find a man with whom she cared to develop a permanent relationship. It wasn't for lack of opportunity, as Charlotte had stated. Most of the men she met failed to meet the standards Kate had in the back of her mind. She didn't think they were too high. There were bound to be men who came close to fulfilling her ideal.

Chase's hard face materialized with crystal clarity in her mind. No! He wasn't the embodiment of her ideal man. He had been a childhood fantasy, and she was a mature woman now, with realistic expectations and down-to-earth qualities that she looked for in a man. Chase Jamison certainly didn't have them.

"We met a very interesting man last night," Charlotte was saying, turned halfway around in her seat to face Kate. "It was after you left with Mark."

Kate listened politely, half of her mind still caught up in the past.

"Chase Jamison," Charlotte carried on, unaware of the jolt that sliced through Kate on hearing the name that had been on her mind for the past twelve hours. "And the woman he was with was Gina Hart." She looked briefly at her husband. "I didn't particularly care for Miss Hart, did you, Ben?"

"I didn't say three words to her," Ben said with typically male logic, "so I couldn't judge her very well."

Charlotte went on blithely. "Well, you know what I mean, Kate. She was so—"

"Gorgeous?" Ben supplied dryly.

"Ben!" She hit his arm playfully. "Anyway, Kate, this Chase Jamison was, to use Ben's word, a gorgeous man. And he was so nice. He was from Texas but was doing the Mardi Gras scene with a group of people that Ben knew, and we spent most of the rest of the evening with them. He and Ben seemed to hit it off after only a few minutes." She turned her gaze on her husband. "What were you talking about?"

Ben shrugged. "Business mostly. He was knowledgeable about shipbuilding. I believe he has a wide variety of interests, and he seemed familiar with Baytown. As a matter of fact, he said he'd been there before."

Kate sat still, as if she'd been turned to stone. Was it only a coincidence that out of all the people at the ball, Chase had managed to make the acquaintance of Ben and Charlotte Scott?

"Did he mention knowing anyone in Baytown?" she asked, her voice sounding foreign in her own ears.

"No," Ben supplied, adding informatively, "but he had noticed your escort's condition."

"Really?" Kate managed faintly.

"I thought it was terribly thoughtful of him," Charlotte said with a knowing smile. "If only you hadn't left with Mark, we could have introduced you, and who knows what might have come of it?"

"I already know Chase Jamison," Kate said baldly.

Charlotte blinked, and Ben's gray eyes sought Kate's in the rear-view mirror.

"He used to live in Baytown, and he worked for my father."

"Oh, Kate," Charlotte breathed in delight.

Kate's mouth thinned. "He is not a nice man, no

matter what your first impression of him might have been. As a matter of fact, he left Langford's under a very serious cloud."

"What kind of cloud?" Charlotte was clearly skeptical.

"Langford's was developing the plans for a prototype vessel, which would have meant the difference between success on a large scale and the mediocre shipyard it is today." A bitter taste was in her mouth as she recalled the facts of Chase's treachery. "The plans disappeared, and Chase turned out to be the prime suspect."

"Is that indisputable fact, Kate?" Ben asked, obviously as taken with Chase as his wife was and reluctant to accept the possibility that his judgment could be at fault.

"If you mean was anything ever proved, or did my father ever press charges, then no." She turned her face away, her eyes picking out familiar landmarks on the interstate. "But just two days after it happened, Chase resigned and left town. We never heard a word from him again."

"Oh, I'm so disappointed!" Charlotte cried. "I liked him so much."

"You and every other woman he ever met," Kate said derisively.

Charlotte's eyes narrowed in sudden interest. "That sounded very personal."

Kate's hands curled impotently into fists, regretting the hasty words. Charlotte was no fool, and she knew Kate better than anyone. She had picked up immediately the emotion behind Kate's remark. Her mind grappled for something to forestall further questions.

"It was all a long time ago, and I had nearly forgotten about it."

"When was this?" the irrepressible Charlotte asked.

Kate heaved a resigned sigh. "I can't recall," she lied. "Several years ago."

"Before you went away to college?"

"Yes."

A thoughtful finger tapped against Charlotte's pursed mouth. "It would have to be at least eight years, then."

Kate remained silent, her eyes trained on passing scenery.

"You couldn't have been more than seventeen, Kate. Did you know him personally? I mean, you said something about women liking him. That doesn't sound like he was just an employee of your father's."

"Charlotte, for Pete's sake!" Ben chided. "Can't you see Kate doesn't want to discuss Chase Jamison?"

Thank you, Ben, Kate mouthed silently. Charlotte had shared many of Kate's secrets ever since they were freshmen together, but even Charlotte had never known about Chase.

"I'm sorry, Kate. All of a sudden I had this feeling that I had stumbled onto something important in your life, something really significant, and I was just barging in without stopping to think first."

"So what else is new," her husband said dryly.

Kate stirred restlessly. "Listen, you two, I'm beginning to think you're making more of this by not knowing the facts than if I just tell you about it."

She leaned back against the cushioned leather, one finger idly tracing the stitching running along the arm rest. "Yes, I did know Chase outside of his capacity as dad's employee. You were right when you sensed something personal in our relationship, Charlotte. I had a crush on Chase from the time I was twelve and he did odd jobs around our house."

Kate could see him now if she closed her eyes. He had been around during the summers, cutting the grass and repairing gadgets, while Kate and her younger brother, Ron, had dogged his tracks like puppies. Then, when he was eighteen, Phillip hired him at the plant. He even made it possible for Chase to attend the state university half of the year and work the other half until he got his degree. By that time, he had moved into a position of authority, with unlimited potential.

Kate's mouth twisted with the bitter memory. Even then, Chase had been a ruthlessly determined person, if only she had had eyes to see it. Of course, Kate had been unaware of the depth of ambition that motivated him. She thought then that Chase Jamison had hung the moon.

By the time she was seventeen, her childish fantasy had deepened into a consuming passion, but although she had been an almost arrogantly self-confident teen, with Chase, she was uncertain, hesitant. He always managed to avoid her attempts to make him notice her. In fact, she always suspected he was secretly laughing at her.

Kate decided to take matters into her own hands late one night in April. Chase often worked late at the shipyard, so she concocted an excuse to go to the plant, determined to bring herself to his attention one way or another. It had been relatively easy. She simply lied to him, saying her father needed to see him at Fox Briar. She drove a new, fast little sports car and persuaded him to allow her to drive him, ignoring the skepticism on his face and feeling a tiny thrill of triumph at having succeeded so far. But the plan hadn't worked out very well after that.

She did not take a direct route to her home but detoured along a beach road and stopped the car under an ancient, sprawling oak tree. Instead of obliging her by treating her like an equal, using the time she had seized for them to explore each other's thoughts and feelings—and whatever else her romantic imaginings may have dreamed up—Chase had been furious. He had taken possession of the car keys before she could react and stormed around the car to yank open the driver's door and shove her aside, announcing that he was driving them back without delay. Kate had never been thwarted before in her life, and she reacted with anger and a flat refusal to leave. She jumped out of the car and refused to get back in.

Her father was a gentle, mild-mannered man, and all the boy friends Kate had collected during her adolescent years had been similar types. Chase was different. Perhaps that was why he sparked such a flame in her. But the role of the aggressor was one he reserved for himself and he reacted in a manner in keeping with the dominant male he was.

"You little fool, maybe you can only learn the hard way," he had muttered almost to himself as his mouth descended on hers in a bruising, punishing kiss.

Surprise and shock held her motionless for a moment, but then, with a whimper of delight, she melted against him, pleased with the results of her scheming.

Faced with her sudden response, Chase had eased the pressure of his mouth, but when she felt him hesitate, she quickly laced her arms around his neck, every instinct urging him to continue the sensual assault. He would have been less than human had he not reacted to the urgency of Kate's eager hands and body as she pressed her young curves against him, wantonly expectant. They dropped to the thick carpet of grass, Kate completely oblivious to the night's heavy dew or to the impropriety of her actions.

"For God's sake, Kate," he had groaned against her hot mouth, "do you know what you're asking for?"

She had not known, but her heart had cried out that she didn't care just as long as he didn't stop, didn't reject her, as he had done so often.

But in the end, he had rejected her. He had come to his senses in time to prevent the inevitable outcome that she had invited, and Kate had been devastated. He had stopped just when her senses were screaming.

She scrambled to her feet. "Chase, why did you stop?" she had cried. "What did I do wrong?"

He swore savagely, collapsing against the car, bending his head and shaking it in a hard, negative movement. Then he had said things to her that she had never forgotten, could never forgive.

"Just what do you think your father would say if he could see you now?" he had scorned, branding her with the angry flash of his eyes. "You're hardly behaving like the lady he has so carefully reared. You act more like the spoiled little girl you really are." There had been more after that, much more.

His words had seared, slashed her pride. He had accused her of selfishness, of not caring who was hurt by any of her actions as long as she got what she wanted.

Kate still winced at the pain and humiliation she had suffered at Chase's words. When he finished, he had driven her back to the plant in a stony silence, and once there, had unfolded his lean frame, his anger a tightly leashed, almost-tangible thing. Without a word to her, he had disappeared inside the Langford plant.

Her eyes, dark blue with remembered pain, gazed unseeingly through the car's window. They were crossing a long stretch of bridge that spanned a marshland teeming with wildlife. She watched a white crane settle gracefully into standing water.

"Maybe I wouldn't have so much hostility for Chase if all he had been guilty of was rejecting the

immature advances of the silly teenager I was then,"
she murmured thoughtfully, "but that was the night
the plans for the prototype were removed from the
safe in dad's office. Only Chase and a couple of other
men had access to them."

"But surely he wasn't suspected just because he
had the opportunity," Charlotte insisted, still determined to find some way to exonerate the man who
had so impressed her the previous night.

"Not exactly." Kate's mouth had a rueful twist.
"But an employee whom my father trusted implicitly
claimed that he saw Chase with the plans. I was as
reluctant as you to believe he was guilty at first. I
thought surely he would come forward and explain
that he had been away from the plant—that he had
been with me and couldn't have taken the plans, but
he didn't."

Ben had been listening quietly. "Why didn't you
tell your father there could be some doubt since he
had been with you? Naturally, Chase would be
reluctant to come forward, using you as an alibi.
Any gentleman would."

Gentleman! If they only knew. There was nothing
gentlemanly about Chase.

"At first, all I could think about was the cruel
things he had said. It had dawned on me that he had
used me to provide himself an alibi for the evening,
and I would have died before lifting a finger to help
him out."

"Sounds like your idea of love was pretty juvenile," Charlotte chided her gently.

Kate laughed humorlessly. "Yes. Well, in the end,
I capitulated and made a confession to my father."

But that hadn't worked out the way she thought it
would, either. Her father simply did not believe her.

"Chase couldn't have taken those plans, daddy.
We were together that night." Perched on a chair in
her father's study, Kate's hands were clasped on her

knees, and under the amusement of Phillip's gaze, she had felt more like an adolescent than the assured young woman she longed to be.

Phillip Langford had risen slowly as he digested Kate's words. "Katie, honey, I realize you want to help Chase, but I'm afraid your rather generous attempt won't do the trick. If Chase had been with you that night, I'm sure he would have mentioned it before now."

Stiffening her arms at her sides, Kate faced her father with mulish determination. "Daddy! I mean it. Chase was with me. I picked him up in my new car, and we drove to the beach." She had paused then, suddenly all too aware of the difficulty of her next revelation. "We stayed at the beach a long time."

A frown entered Phillip's features. "What do you mean, a long time?" he asked quietly.

Kate turned away from the sternness in her father's eyes. "I mean just that. We were at the beach a long time. Chase couldn't have taken those plans, if they were taken when your impeccable source claims they were taken, because he was with me!" she finished in a rush.

Phillip's brow cleared again, and a tiny smile hovered near his mouth. "And what were you doing, honey?" An amused brow lifted as he searched her flushed face.

"Daddy, I can see you don't believe me, but it's true. I . . . I guess Chase didn't say anything because he wanted to protect my name." She darted a glance toward her father and couldn't prevent the surge of annoyance that rose as she saw the patent skepticism on his face.

Phillip laughed. "And, as I said, Kate, what were you and Chase doing on the beach at midnight when your grandmother and I apparently assumed you were in bed?"

All caution fled at the amusement lacing her father's words. "We were making love, if you must know, daddy."

Phillip's expression barely changed. He was shaking his head in exasperated amusement. He sank back into his chair and made an effort to school his features. "I know you think you are doing Chase a favor, Kate, but you really mustn't take such incredible steps to help him. Darling, he's a man who can handle most situations, and if he chooses not to divulge information which could possibly clear his name in this mess, then we've no choice but to accept his decision."

Kate had never discussed that awful weekend and its consequences with anyone before, and just thinking about it now brought it all back with painful clarity. She rubbed her thumb and forefinger tiredly against her temples. A dull throbbing had developed into a raging headache. "So now you know why the less I see of Chase Jamison, the better off I will be."

A thoughtful silence descended while Ben negotiated the familiar streets through Baytown. The thought of her own room and the peaceful view of the Gulf that it commanded beckoned invitingly. She was beginning to feel slightly uncomfortable over revealing what she saw as an unattractive glimpse of herself, but the Scotts had obviously been taken in by Chase. There was no denying he had a lot of charm. Anybody would be impressed if he chose to release the full battery of his intelligence and good looks, and he had obviously chosen to do that the previous night. Ben and Charlotte had succumbed.

Kate shifted restlessly on the smooth leather upholstery. Right now, instead of feeling justified at having informed them of Chase's true character, she was aware of a keen sense of disloyalty. She told herself it was ridiculous. She owed nothing to Chase, absolutely nothing. Actually, the debt was his. Still, she was not able to shake off the feeling that somehow she had betrayed Chase.

Fox Briar, set back from the winding street beneath moss-draped live oaks, was a welcome sight. It was a relief to escape from the confinement of the car.

"Thanks again, you two," she called as Ben settled back behind the wheel after unloading her luggage.

Charlotte leaned around him. "Let's have lunch in a day or so."

Kate nodded. "Right. I'll give you a call when I've had a chance to go through the mess on my desk." She shifted the overnight case in one hand and secured a better hold on the folded canvas garment bag, which contained most of her clothes. "No, never mind, Ben. I can manage." She stopped him as he prepared to get out of the car again.

Reluctantly, he allowed her to manage the weight of her luggage alone. Kate did not turn as the sound of the car faded around the drive and through the trees.

Her gaze fell lovingly on Fox Briar's distinctive front façade. Huge, inverted Y-shaped stairs led to the main entrance of the house. Ground level contained an informal living area along with the kitchen and sunroom toward the rear of the house. Formal entrance foyer and living room were located on the upper floor. The design was common to many homes built in the South when labor was plentiful.

Kate dropped her luggage at the bottom of the stairs. She and Fanny, cook and housekeeper at Fox Briar for all of Kate's life and longer, could bring them in later. Right now, all she wanted was two aspirins and a glass of iced tea. Forsaking the imposing front entrance, Kate went around the side of the house along a brick paved walkway and reached for the knob of the back door.

"Kate! Thank God you're home." Olivia Langford's face was wreathed in lines of strain.

"What's the matter, Livvy?" Her grandmother was usually placidly unmoved by circumstances that overwhelmed most people. Kate's heart thumped sickeningly as she stared into the unnaturally pale face of the woman who had been mother and much more to her.

"It's Phillip, Kate. They've just called from his office. He's been taken to the hospital."

"Is it serious?" The question was unnecessary. She could tell by the expression on Livvy's face.
"Yes. I was just leaving. We'd better hurry."

Chapter Three

"I can't believe this. I know there is a mistake somewhere." Kate's eyes, wide and incredulous, were wet as she struggled for composure. She turned to her grandmother.

"Did you know dad's plans, Livvy?"

The old lady sighed, watching Kate's face and seeing the slight tremor of her lips. "I knew Phillip was considering something, Kate. You know, trying to keep the business afloat was getting to be almost more than he could handle. A group of investors had expressed interest in purchasing all of Langford's holdings. It seems they planned to modernize equipment and methods. Really, Phillip's approach had remained practically unchanged since Joshua ran the business."

Kate jumped up agitatedly. "You know dad was trying desperately to salvage the business, Livvy. How can you criticize him now?" She made a determined effort to control the tremulous movement of her mouth. "And you can bet that it won't be only methods and equipment that will be changed when a bunch of strangers take over. People will go." Her voice broke. "Oh, Livvy, there must be a way out of this."

"I'm afraid not, Kate. And don't keep on distressing yourself. What's done is done."

Striding to the window, which overlooked the Gulf, Kate inhaled deeply, making an effort to follow her grandmother's advice. It was difficult to control the emotions that had consumed her since she'd learned the full extent of the change in her life. The shock of her father's death only hours after being stricken with a massive heart attack had plunged everyone into a state of uncertainty. After the initial shock, only Livvy had seemed to retain an unflappability, which Kate now envied. Her grandmother had borne the loss of her only son with a philosophical acceptance that Kate could only presume came from her great age.

Kate's gaze moved to rest moodily on her brother. Ron's shoulders drooped disconsolately. His slight frame was draped on the deep-cushioned sofa, chin resting against his chest. Her eyes narrowed watching him. The two years between them had always seemed far more to Kate, as her personality was so much stronger than Ron's. Her keen business sense overshadowed her brother's lukewarm interest in the family business as well, so that she suspected she would not have an ally in Ron should she try to overturn the action her father had taken just days before his death. Kate saw with sudden clarity that her brother's personality was very similar to their father's. Both lacked the keen competitiveness that Joshua Langford, Olivia's husband and founder of Langford Marine, had had in abundance. It dawned on her that she was the only one feeling this almost unbearable sense of loss that the family business was gone forever. For forty years, boats and yachts, seagoing vessels of various types, had been constructed in the shipyard that bore her family's name. Now that legacy was slipping through her fingers.

"Did you know about this, Ron?" She eyed him sharply, giving voice to the suspicion that lingered, watching a dull flush spread over his thin features. Whereas before she had suspected depression and a natural grief over the loss they had both sustained, Kate now wondered if Ron might be feeling guilty. He shifted uneasily to a more erect position.

"Actually, Kate, dad did mention it to me." Ron rubbed a hand over his face warily, and Kate noted idly the sturdy capability of his fingers. Ron's passion for machinery was well known. He was always tinkering, preferring the solitude of his workshop to the daily challenge of managing the shipyard. There simply wasn't time to devote to the trial and error of the kind of work Ron preferred.

She slammed her open palm violently against the windowsill. "Was I the only one to be kept in ignorance?" she cried, outrage and hurt warring within her chest so that it felt as though a steel band was squeezing her heart.

Her brother rose from the sofa, a little wary as he watched Kate. "That isn't how it was at all, Kate. Dad was going to speak to you soon. He told me he was worried how you would react. He knew that of all of us, you were the one person who wanted to see the Langford family retain ownership of the business." He touched her stiff shoulders tentatively. "Isn't that true, Kate? Wouldn't you have met the announcement that he planned to sell with a full-blown campaign designed to change his mind?"

Kate gazed blindly through the glass, resisting the logic in Ron's words. "I can't understand why you can't see it the way I do, Ronnie. Langford Marine is our birthright, the heritage of other generations—not just yours and mine. We can run it successfully; I know we can. Why did you let him do it?" The look she turned on her brother was both accusing and wounded, causing him to flush uncomfortably. He looked toward his grandmother in silent appeal.

"Ron is right, Kate," the old lady counseled. "You won't be able to see it right now, of course, but I'm sure Phillip had your best interests at heart when he sold out. He didn't want you and Ron to feel the burden of responsibility toward the business and the lives that are influenced by its success or failure. I believe he wanted to free you from what he considered a cross that he was forced to bear. He wasn't like his own father, and he didn't feel the sheer exhilaration and challenge which Joshua thrived on." Her lined face softened with remembrance, and Kate could almost see the misty memories that recalling her husband's strong personality evoked. "I think your father recognized a kindred spirit in Ron." She smiled wisely at him, tolerant of the unhappiness that lingered in the line of his mouth. Her gaze moved to Kate.

"He probably understood your feelings, too, Kate, but he knew that it was going to take more than your determination and spirit to keep the business afloat. Namely, a hefty injection of capital, something we are short of right now. I truly believe he hoped you would see his solution—passing the reins to hardheaded investors and proven businessmen—as the only reasonable thing to do."

Tears welled in Kate's eyes. "I know dad didn't enjoy managing the business, but I was steadily relieving some of the pressure from him." She turned an earnest face to Olivia. "If only he could have waited a little while longer, Livvy. I am good at my job. I can handle the responsibility."

Her grandmother nodded wryly. "You have more than proved that, darling. It wasn't that you were short of talent. Phillip was running out of time."

Kate wiped the palms of her hands across wet cheeks. Her eyes, midnight blue, held a rueful light. "You make me feel a selfish brat, Livvy, thinking only of the effect of all this on me. The whole family is affected, and both of you have been much more, well, human."

"Kate, you exaggerate," Olivia protested in mild exasperation. "We're all shocked and grieved, and we react according to our own natures. I for one would be very worried about you, young lady, if you turned into a shrinking violet under this. Why, you're a credit to the Langfords and my own darling Joshua. I just wish he could have lived to see the woman you've turned out to be."

Kate smiled shakily and hugged her grandmother impulsively. "You are a sweetheart, Livvy, always managing to say just the right thing." She turned to Ron, brief apology flashing in her smile. "Do you intend to stay with the company, Ronnie?"

He met her gaze with an indecisive shrug of his shoulders. "I haven't decided what I'm going to do, Kate. Perhaps when they send the new president, I'll be able to tell within a short time whether or not I want to stick around. It's all up in the air right now as far as I'm concerned."

Kate marveled at her brother's attitude. More than once during the past few months she had felt an overwhelming urge to lift Ron bodily and shake some life into him. He had a responsible position at the shipyard, and as uncomfortable as the thought was, she was convinced he would not have that particular job if he were anyone other than the son of Phillip Langford. If he would only show half the interest in his work as he displayed in his experiments with new types of engines. No amount of research or time devoted to whatever current project he was involved in was too much trouble, but it was nothing that could be applied to boats, as Kate had lamented frequently.

Her father's decision to sell might possibly offer Ron an opportunity to devote all of his time to what Kate had considered only a hobby. They each would realize some capital from the transaction, but on second thought, it was hardly enough to subsidize Ron's uncertain type of venture.

"I wonder who the new owners will put into the top job," she murmured absently, rubbing a slim forefinger against a firmly rounded chin. Her gaze was once more drawn to the wide window and the incessant movement of the Gulf.

Olivia rose from the delicate chair she had been occupying. "Actually, I believe I can answer that," she said with a meaningful light in her eyes.

Kate turned quickly, a puzzled line appearing between the delicate arch of her tawny brows. "Who, Livvy?"

"Chase Jamison."

Realization hit Kate like a body blow, and she was motionless for a moment, staring at her grandmother. Quickly, she leaned forward to touch a graceful crystal bird that rested on the table under the window so that her thick sun-streaked hair fell like a curtain to obscure her face.

"Not the Chase Jamison we used to know?" With an effort, she managed to make the question sound casual, already knowing the answer. Suddenly, all mystery regarding Chase's announced intention to return to Baytown was removed.

A pleased smile played around the old lady's lips. "As a matter of fact, it is the same Chase we used to know," she cheerfully acknowledged, expecting the news to bring nothing but pleasure. "Isn't it an amazing coincidence?"

Ron was unabashedly pleased at the news. "How is it that Chase is going to come back? The last I heard, he was making his fortune in Texas."

Had Chase been in Texas? Kate had never heard his name mentioned after that awful incident. But she didn't allow her thoughts to begin wandering that familiar path. Resolutely, she concentrated her attention on Livvy.

"He's one of the investors and has a personal interest in implementing some innovative new procedures in this yard," Olivia explained. "I always thought he was a fine boy and that he had a promising future." She frowned slightly, her wrinkled face pensive. "It was very unfortunate that we had to lose him over that terrible business regarding the plans." Her bright gaze rested on her grandchildren. "I knew him as a youngster, and he couldn't have done anything dishonorable, no matter how overwhelming the evidence against him might have seemed." With a beringed hand, she stroked her chin absently. "Phillip went to extraordinary lengths to defend Chase. He had such confidence in the boy, treating him almost like a son." Her gaze strayed beyond the window. "With Chase's undoubted ability, he would have made an excellent manager for the shipyard within a few years."

Kate's eyes saw nothing as she listened to Olivia's unstinting praise of the man who seemed to have infiltrated every corner of her life in a few short weeks. "What about me?" she asked through stiff lips. "Didn't I figure in any long-range plans of my father's?"

A wry twist of her mouth revealed Olivia's response to the wounded pride evident in Kate's words. "You will have to understand, dear, that

Phillip naturally assumed you would marry. The chances of your staying here and being a part of the family business were very slim. Although it may seem unfair, Phillip strongly believed that daughters do not carry on family businesses, even though that philosophy may seem outdated to you."

Kate couldn't bear hearing any more and moved toward the door. "How about some coffee?" She turned a set face toward the two, a brow raised inquiringly, refusing to acknowledge the hurt her grandmother's revelations had uncovered. When they nodded, she escaped thankfully to the kitchen.

So at last she had the reason behind Chase's cryptic remarks Sunday night. He wasn't just coming home. He was returning with a vengeance. Somehow he had managed to move into her world, and although he was not even there yet, his overwhelming personality was making itself known. There was no mistaking Olivia's and Ron's reaction, while at work she already suspected his influence would be overlaid onto the entire operation. The irony of it was that everyone seemed grateful to him for it. Everyone except me, she qualified firmly. Her mouth set in a stubborn line, which her family was all too familiar with. He could think again if he thought his charm would have the same effect on her. She had learned her lesson long before, and she had learned it well.

Mechanically, she made the coffee, filling the pot with cold water, measuring the grounds and flipping the switch on, all the while seething with a cold rage. It was bad enough that her father had followed through on a momentous decision to sell the business without a hint to her, but to sell it to Chase Jamison! She was racked by a feeling so intense that her hands shook as they handled the coffee cups, clinking noisily on the tray.

Her grandmother, sweet, unsuspecting darling that she was, might see Chase as a wronged man, but she knew better. He was calculating and cruel. A man as unfeeling as she knew him to be would hardly hesitate to act dishonorably if he knew he would benefit. Hadn't she personal knowledge of a side of Chase that he kept well hidden from those he wished to retain a good image of him? She still winced when she remembered the contempt and scorn he had displayed toward her. Suppose he felt that way about her whole family? What real proof did any of them have that he didn't despise them all?

She looked down at her fingers, clenched whitely against the edge of the counter. She inhaled deeply, then lifted the coffeepot. She poured the brew carefully into three cups, sweetened her grandmother's and picked up the tray.

Both Olivia and Ron looked up as she entered the room, placing the tray on a small table in front of the sofa. She cleared her throat in uncharacteristic nervousness.

"When do you think Chase will arrive to pick up the reins?" In spite of the carefully worded question, it came out sounding just short of sarcasm.

Her grandmother's sharp perception was alerted. "Surely you agree that Chase Jamison's decision to manage the yard personally is definitely to our advantage?" she inquired with a frown.

Kate lowered her mouth gingerly to the rim of the cup. "What makes you so certain this is Chase's decision?" she retorted. "Surely he's only taking orders from the investors?"

Olivia's delicate snort drew surprised interest from her audience. "Chase *is* the major investor. It's his company which has purchased the business." She turned a wryly raised brow to her granddaughter. "And when you've had time to consider the situation from all angles, Kate, I'm certain you will feel only gratitude to Chase."

Gratitude! Kate almost choked. She jumped up from her chair, sloshing coffee onto the cream-colored carpet. "Oh, look what I've done!" She leaned over, thankful for the curtain of her thick hair and began to press her napkin onto the stain.

"What's the matter with you, Kate?" Ron's less sensitive antennae had finally noted his sister's agitation. "You needn't feel nervous about meeting Chase again. If you're worried he'll recall what pests we both were when he used to work here at Fox Briar, then forget it. Even if he did, he's the type of man who lives only in the present. He'll probably accept you for the astute businesswoman you are now, especially after he has seen you in action for a couple of days."

Ron's words meant to offer sympathetic comfort, only compounded the mixture of emotions Kate was struggling with. He probably thought her last contact with Chase had been when he worked at their home when he was a teenager.

"Livvy, how did it actually happen that Chase ever left the business?" Ron's voice interrupted Kate's thoughts, drawing her reluctant attention to Livvy's defense of Chase. "I was at boarding school at the time and never did understand exactly what happened," Ron was saying.

Olivia's brow puckered, making an effort to recall the circumstances. "I believe Chase was working long hours during that particular time. The company had a contract to produce some specially equipped fiberglass hydroplanes. The designs for highspeed craft were developed at considerable expense by the engineers on the staff, and their design drawings were being kept secret, secured in a vault which only a few people could open." The old lady lifted the delicate china cup and sipped thoughtfully. "Chase, of course, was among those who had the combination. On the night it happened, he was the only person on the premises who could have opened the safe. At any rate, the drawings disappeared, and the redesign took several months of painstaking rework. It was enough so that the edge which Langford's had to produce the prototype was lost, and consequently, a very large profit which we had hoped to realize on the project never materialized." She smiled ruefully. "Some of our competitors managed to develop the same product amazingly similar to the missing plans."

An unbelieving scowl replaced the usually placid lines of Ron's face. "You mean Chase was fired just on that flimsy—I hate to call it evidence."

"Your father questioned Chase about his whereabouts during the evening after getting a report from a trusted source who claimed to have seen him leaving the plant with the plans."

"Who was this trusted source?" With obvious skepticism, Ron watched while Olivia set her cup onto the table.

"Phillip never revealed his source."

"Never?"

"It would have served no purpose, as Chase resigned abruptly."

Incredulously, Ron looked into his grandmother's eyes, then transferred his gaze to Kate, who had remained tensely silent during the conversation.

"I know all this happened a long time ago, but it seems to me pretty unfair to have canned a damn good man just on the hearsay evidence of a single source, no matter how reliable he may have seemed," he added astringently.

"Really, Ron, what does it matter now?" Kate

had been dabbing at the coffee stain on the carpet but now rose to her feet, giving the two a view of her straight back as she disappeared toward the kitchen.

Olivia and Ron exchanged glances. "I think it matters," he said quietly as she returned with a bottle of spray cleaner in one hand and a sponge in another. "I think Chase may have been railroaded out of town without having a chance to defend himself."

Kate turned to him suddenly, her eyes a deep indigo. "He had a chance to defend himself, and he said nothing!" Her voice was low, but emotion threaded through it, causing a tremor in her words. "Nothing, Ron. I even told dad—" She stopped, appalled at what she had almost revealed.

Ron frowned. "You told dad what?" he questioned. "What did you have to do with it, Kate?"

She turned a forbidding shoulder to the interested looks on both faces, spraying the stain on the carpet. "Nothing. Just forget it. It was all over years ago, anyway, so just forget it." She straightened quickly, looking neither at her grandmother nor Ron, whose faces reflected their puzzlement. She headed for the kitchen, grinding her teeth in a wave of self-disgust. If she had wished to arouse curiosity regarding her role in the events of that evening, then she had certainly succeeded.

Kate replaced the cleanser and tidily hung the cloth on a rack to dry. Facing the window, she pressed her palms to both cheeks in a childishly ineffective effort to cool her heated skin. Why was she letting herself become so emotional over something that had happened more than eight years before? And why was she still feeling such hostility toward a man whom she should have forgotten, now that she was a woman with a highly developed self-esteem and proven professional accomplishments to her credit?

A niggling little voice in the back of her mind said that Chase Jamison's criticism so many years before had been instrumental in the path her development had taken. True, it had been a searing, stinging assessment, but it had forced her into examining herself, and she had not liked some of the things she discovered. So why the hostility now? She shook the tawny mane of her hair, the tiny crease between her brows expressing her inability to arrive at an answer to the riddle, and sighed.

She turned toward the door, hoping Livvy and Ron had found some other topic of conversation, shrugging in resignation when she entered the room and heard Chase's name.

". . . incredible that it could have happened, but Phillip was so relieved and pleased that it was all he could talk about when he got back." Olivia was speaking as Kate moved to collect the coffee cups, determined to ignore the conversation.

"You were away at college then, I believe, Kate."

Kate looked up and frowned. "When?"

"When Phillip ran into Chase at a—"

Kate released an exasperated sigh. "Really, Livvy. Aren't you ever going to tire of discussing Chase Jamison? I, for one, am sick of hearing his name!" She clattered the delicate cups on the tray, treating them with an unusually careless disregard.

Olivia tutted disapprovingly, and Ron stared in amazement. Kate's mouth set in a stubborn line, uncaring of their reactions.

"What is it with you, Kate?" Ron's gaze surveyed her set face, and Kate wished she had exercised more control over her tongue. She could almost hear the wheels turning in Ron's head as he searched for some explanation for her temper.

She was saved from having to explain the inexplicable. Olivia moved toward the door purposefully. "Ron, you promised to drive me into town to pick up some cards at the stationery shop," she said in the sudden silence. "I'm ready to go now."

Her firm tone left no room for refusal, and Ron turned reluctantly after directing one more penetrating look at Kate. Still perplexed, he lingered. "Kate, if you—"

"Ron," Olivia prompted with an imperious tone. With a final puzzled glance in Kate's direction, Ron went out.

No more than ten minutes had passed when a car door slammed, shattering the quiet of the afternoon and Kate's bitter introspection. It was stupid to allow her temper to get the better of her, especially over events that were thankfully in the past and if she had anything to do with it, she vowed fervently, would remain there.

She was vaguely aware of the rusty squeak of the ancient iron gate that led from the driveway to the pathway around the side of the house. Whoever it was intended using the kitchen entrance, Kate thought idly, hoping the turmoil of her emotions was masked by the carefully polite expression she pinned on her face.

She quickly placed the used cups in the dishwasher and stored the tray in a pantry. She was turning away, her thoughts still cloudy and emotional, when the visitor appeared at the door. She could see an outline through the glass, but she couldn't see his face, only that he was tall and broad. She forced down the sudden pang that darted against her heart. Thinking of Chase was making her fanciful, and it had been a long time since she had been guilty of that. Warily, she rubbed palms down gently curved thighs, the feel of the soft denim comfortingly ordinary, and moved to the door.

She pulled it open just as his hand was raised to press the old-fashioned button that sounded a jangling bell in the kitchen. For a moment, she could only stare, mouth parted, eyes wide.

"Hello, Kate."

Chapter Four

Somewhere in the back of her mind, Kate railed against the injustice of meeting Chase again where the advantage was his. She had needed to be prepared before facing him, preferably in her office, not at home. No, never there, where Fanny the cook had supplied them with thousands of cookies and gallons of lemonade and iced tea on hot afternoons.

"What are you doing here?" Her voice came out husky and uneven.

His eyes made a thoroughly male assessment of her tautly held figure. "Taking a walk down memory lane?" He braced lazily against the frame, his leanly muscled body exuding an overwhelming masculinity, still possessing that pervasive maleness that triggered a reluctant response from her even then.

Swiftly, her gaze moved over his hard features. Eight years had wrought some changes, but they had only intensified the compellingly attractive man he had become. Her eyes registered the chiseled hardness of his features, dropping to the sensual mouth, more cynical now, but the firm, jutting chin had the same arrogant decisiveness that had been so effective in quelling her schoolgirl impulsiveness. Her gaze swept upward to encounter the taut, leashed quality in his expression and ricocheted away. She wrenched her thoughts into line. What interpretation would he put on her long, drawn-out appraisal? The worst, no doubt, she thought, answering her own question.

"I don't think we have anything to talk about, Chase," she said with as much finality as she could manage.

For a moment, he just looked at her, the rich brown of his eyes reflecting nothing that she could indentify, only a cool indifference. She moved warily, and he advanced before she could react, stepping inside and closing the door with the palm of his hand, never taking his eyes from her face.

Her temper flared at his arrogance in invading her home without an invitation, but she knew from past experience how futile an exercise it would be to argue with him, so she swallowed whatever angry words had been trembling on her lips and made an attempt to regain her composure.

"Since we have nothing to talk about," she reasserted coldly, "I suppose you couldn't wait before coming here to gloat."

His expression hardened at her choice of words, and for a moment, Kate felt she had perhaps gone too far. But what she was feeling was nothing more than mild caution, she told herself bracingly. She had no reason to be intimidated by the firm line of his jaw or the glint in his eye.

"Strangely enough," he returned, "I considered it best to present myself to you before we met in the board room, so to speak." A wry mockery laced his words, making her feel foolishly juvenile, but there was nothing but grim determination on his face as he shouldered past her, looking familiarly around the room.

"Do come in," she invited dryly.

One expressive brow lifted as he folded his long length into one of the chairs that matched the glass-topped breakfast table. "As to my coming here to Fox Briar," he went on smoothly, "I have as much right to be here as you."

Kate's lips parted speechlessly, and for a moment, she thought her reaction caused Chase's eyes to narrow slightly. "What . . . what do you mean?" She leaned against the counter, oblivious of the sharp edge digging into her hip.

He ignored her question, looking around alertly. "Is Olivia home? You're still living together, aren't you? Olivia and Ron and you?"

She stared blankly. "Of course we still live together. We're a family. Where else would we go?" Kate grappled with a confusing sense of bewilderment, as if the conversation were being carried on at more than one level. She was swept by a sudden inexplicable anxiety, and she knew with a sense of helplessness that in any encounter with Chase she was still hopelessly ill equipped to win.

"Are you alone?" he prompted, somehow giving an impression of aggressive masculinity even though he remained seated.

Olivia and Ron left a few minutes ago." She supplied the information with only half a mind, her quick intelligence working furiously for some clue as to his motive for being there and trying at the same time to fathom his earlier remarks. "You said you have a right to be at Fox Briar," she persisted, feeling far from calm but trying to conceal it from him. "What did you mean?"

Chase drove the fingers of one hand through the chestnut brown of his hair, its disturbed texture lending a dangerous rakishness to his appearance. "I've been in town a few days," he began on a deep indrawn breath, "and I purposely avoided showing up here until you had had a chance to come to grips with . . . everything." His eyes caught and held hers. "I'm truly sorry about your father, Kate. Phillip was a fine man. No one knows that better than me."

Kate's eyes stung, but she swallowed the thickness that burgeoned in her throat. "Thank you . . . but would you please explain what you meant about Fox Briar?" Only a slight huskiness showed in her voice, and she straightened, moving away from the support of the counter, steeled to hear what she was now convinced would be yet another blow in the almost never-ending series of shocks that she had withstood lately.

Chase eyed her sharply, as though trying to decide whether her confusion was genuine. He leaned back, raking a hand over his mouth. "I thought by now you would have been furnished a complete account-ing of the situation," he stated. "The trustees were given ample time to effect the transition. Hell, it's been over two weeks since they gave me their report."

She moved her head in blank bewilderment. "I don't know what you're talking about. What trus-tees? Are you talking about your company . . . I mean the company that purchased the plant?"

He stood with sudden purpose, drawing up to her so that she caught her lip between her teeth, backing away slightly to combat the wariness that settled somewhere in her stomach when he was too near. "I thought it would be a good idea to discuss with you"—he paused,—"all of you, Olivia and Ron as well, the situation which exists. In the purchase, we acquired more than just the shipyard facility, Kate. It seems old Joshua Langford tied his real estate holdings as well as other financial investments into the corporation. When the assets were reviewed, Fox Briar was included in the final transaction."

"I don't believe dad would enter into a contract which would deprive us of Fox Briar," Kate began stiffly.

Chase studied her for several long, measuring seconds. "With all due respect to Phillip, he was not a very astute businessman. It wasn't his nature to scrutinize contracts or to display much interest in fine print."

Kate's mouth twisted bitterly, unwilling to acknowledge the accuracy of his words. "And, of course, he was well aware that he was selling out to you, and that would have made him even more trusting, Chase. Isn't that what you counted on?" The full import of what he was revealing was finally sinking in. Kate actually swayed with the realization, and Chase's hand closed around the soft flesh of her arm. She jerked away, an inexplicable panic rising in her at his touch.

His hand fell away. "I know you won't believe this, but it was not my intent to swindle anyone, and as for the fact that Fox Briar was tied to the corporation, it was probably done for tax purposes, possibly a shelter which Joshua felt was necessary. It was years ago, and he never actually reversed the action, and neither did Phillip."

Her gaze lifted to the window above the sink, moving beyond the bright pink oleanders that flanked the side of the house and on out toward a grove of oaks standing placidly in the endless green of the grounds. "What does this mean?" she whispered, a terrible dread tightening her chest.

He moved behind her, but his voice sounded distant and remote. "That's what I came to talk about. There's no need for you to adopt that desolate air. I haven't come to deprive you of your childhood home, evicting grandmother, baby brother and pets." His sarcasm lashed her already bruised spirit.

"Then why have you come?"

His face was hard. "I told you. I thought we should discuss the . . . uh, arrangements."

She frowned. "Arrangements?"

He hunched his shoulders irritably. "Yes. I don't intend to displace you or the members of your family, but I do have to have a place to live, and I have a legal right to use Fox Briar."

She stared for a moment; then realization dawned on her. "Are you saying that you actually intend to move into this house? That we are going to have to live together?"

He smiled, baring his teeth so that she thought of a stalking tiger.

"Live together?" he repeated, as though trying out the words. "That does have a nice ring to it."

Kate's hands were on her hips, outrage flashing in her eyes. "Would you please stop beating around the bush and tell me just exactly what it is you plan?"

He reseated himself at the table, a relaxed nonchalance in the powerful lines of his body. "It's simple enough, Kate. Fox Briar is a large, rambling estate. There are six acres, and the corporation owns it, if you get my drift."

Kate smiled bitterly. "I see, I think. Because of our changed circumstances"—her mouth flexed derisively on the words—"we either dance to your tune, or we're going to find ourselves on the street. Do I have that right?"

Chase raised his head and stared directly into her eyes. "It's about what you'd expect from me, isn't it?"

For the life of her, Kate was at a loss to interpret his attitude. Frowning uncertainly, she tried again.

"If I was wrong, then I beg your pardon." With difficulty, she refrained from sounding sarcastic. "And if so, why don't you explain just what your plans are."

She faced him, the indigo of her eyes touching the well-shaped curve of his mouth, then skittering away. She knew Chase was aware of her feelings, the humiliation of finding him of all people in a position to dictate to her family.

Picking up on her own momentary lapse, his gaze dropped to her slightly tremulous mouth. "What's the matter, Kate?" All of a sudden, his voice deepened with a pervasive sensuality. "You seem a bit hostile, but I remember a time when you couldn't get enough of me." His voice had taken on a husky note.

A deep flush stained her cheeks. Helplessly, she acknowledged Chase's ability to reduce her dignity to shreds by his casual reference to her tempestuous behavior when she was seventeen. She drew a deep, calming breath.

"I might have expected some attempt to drag up recollections of my silly behavior years ago," she said, forcing her eyes to withstand the knowing glint in his, "but it won't do you any good, Chase. Even though you may think you are in a superior position, it still doesn't give you the right to ridicule me or my family's name, considering the part you played. My actions that night were the result of honest emotions, while your behavior was the despicable act of a . . . a traitor and a thief!" She pressed shaking hands tightly against her thighs. Thank heaven he couldn't know just how devastating those moments in his arms had been to her or how equally shattering his scathing criticism had been.

"If you're referring to the plans which I allegedly ripped off, then don't be an idiot, Kate. You know I didn't take anything that belonged to Langford's that night." His mouth curled in a slow smile. "Although I was tempted."

His double meaning was not lost on Kate. She strove to contain the hot words trembling on her tongue, her agitation increasing. "I wish you would refrain from reminding me of that night. It must have afforded you a lot of amusement, but I can only thank God you disappeared even if in leaving you showed a deplorable lack of appreciation for everything my father did for you."

A shuttered expression hid Chase's reaction, and he turned away, his broad back and the taut line of his hips reminding her aginst her will of that awful night.

"My debt to Phillip was squared years ago," he said shortly.

"What do you mean?"

He turned his head, slanting a sardonic look at her puzzlement. "What is this?" he drawled. "Don't tell me there's something you haven't been informed of in the internal workings of the business?"

"Stop it, Chase!" she countered impatiently. "How did you square yourself with my father?"

He moved again, coming up close to her. "Never mind, little wildcat," he taunted. "It's all water under the bridge now."

Kate inhaled sharply, resisting the immediate response to his teasing charm, and forcibly reminded herself of Chase's true opinion of her. For reasons of his own, he was back in Baytown, and even more mystifying, he was treating her as though he had forgotten his cruel assessment of her character.

"Whatever your plans are, Chase, I know you can't possibly want to live in close proximity to me." Her lip curled, firming the threatening wobble of her chin. "Your opinion couldn't have changed that much that you could tolerate living in the same house with a spoiled brat like me, could it? I haven't forgotten your words, even if you choose to."

Chase's face remained impassive, but a glint in his eyes etched a tiny crease between her brows. What was he up to?

"I'm older now, and so are you," he retorted, blatant sexuality in the look he swept over her. "Perhaps I will find you more tolerable than I did then."

She clicked her tongue angrily, lifting her chin so that only the smooth line of her throat and the delicate molding of her jaw were visible to his gaze. Her heart was thudding in response to the sensual tone of his voice as well as the look in his eye. "It doesn't matter," she snapped. "That was a long time ago, and I paid it the amount of attention it deserved —none," she said, vowing he would never learn the true impact his casually administered lesson had made.

"You never did know how to take constructive criticism," he informed her grimly.

She spun around. "Constructive! You meant to hurt me, Chase, but I consigned your advice to the devil. And you as well. That silly, impressionable teenager doesn't exist anymore. Neither does all that hero worship I lavished on you." She was trembling with reaction.

Anger carved two white lines beside Chase's mouth, and his eyes were a clear, cold amber. No trace of the usual laid-back charm of a moment before was evident. His eyes raked the length of her in a contemptuous arc. "It seems you've learned nothing, then. Your current playmate no doubt appreciates your generosity."

"Who?" Kate responded sharply, caught off guard.

"Mark Devereaux." A sardonic flex of his mouth demonstrated clearly his opinion of Mark as a suitor.

Vexed that she had allowed her temper to flare beyond her control, Kate breathed slowly to gain a minute to cope with this maddening man.

"How is he as a lover?" Chase drawled outrageously. "They say too much alcohol renders a man—"

"Will you shut up!" Kate raged. "It's none of your business what my relationship with Mark is, and besides, you're mistaken about him being my—" She broke off abruptly as she realized she was furnishing Chase information that was none of his business. Besides, all of a sudden, Mark's undemanding affection began to seem preferable to the disturbing effects of Chase Jamison on her nervous system. She began again. "I'm not going to quarrel with you, Chase. I'm sure we can agree on that."

His eyes rested on her heated cheeks. Amusement lurked in his gaze. "For once, our feelings are mutual, then," he declared.

"If you mean you want to see as little of me as possible, then yes, the feeling is mutual." Confused and more than a little bewildered, she crossed her arms against her stomach, against the churning inside that threatened to erupt any moment.

"Well, that wasn't exactly what I meant, but it seems we are stuck with each other," Chase admitted, a slant to his sensual mouth, "whether we like it or not."

Her gaze flew to his and bounced away, skipping restlessly off other objects in the room. Why couldn't she meet him eye to eye?

"I've done my homework as far as the business is concerned, and I know your position there is a vital one." Any hint of the latent sexuality of a moment before was gone as he launched coolly into the matter that had been hanging between them since his arrival. "You're hardly an administrative assistant," he added, stressing her job title and inferring more with his tone than he actually said.

"Now what are you insinuating?"

He swore impatiently. "Oh, knock it off, Kate! Your father allowed you to assume more and more responsibility in your job. In reality, there are half a dozen men whose titles would indicate their position outranks yours at Langford Marine, including Ben Scott, but my inquiries have revealed that administrative assistant is hardly the proper designation for the power you wield. Clearly, only Phillip's authority outweighed your own." He jammed his hands into his jeans, pulling the fabric tautly over his flat stomach, and Kate's eyes were hastily averted. She needed no obvious reminders of his virility. The lithe muscles of his body were indelibly imprinted on her memory.

"If what you say is true," Kate said, making no effort to deny it, "then there have been no complaints."

Chase jerked his shoulders impatiently. "No, of course there were no complaints. Traditionally, ship-building is a male-dominated field; however, you have proved more than capable. I only wonder how long it would have been before you took over completely."

Kate's outraged gasp seemed to sail right over his head. "You chauvinistic beast! Are you suggesting that there is anything wrong with the fact that I was advancing in my job in spite of the fact that I'm only a woman?" Her words were heavy with sarcasm. "Or perhaps you're implying that I succeeded because Phillip Langford was my father?" She speared him with a blue stare. "Which is it, Chase?"

He turned suddenly, pressing a tanned hand against the back of his powerful neck. "I'm suggesting neither, as you well know. I'm simply stating that

I'm aware of the extent of your involvement in the company, which I will be running starting Monday morning. I'm also requesting your cooperation. I'm going to need your help. You know better than anyone how extremely precarious the situation is at Langford's. One major setback could cause the company to go completely under." He faced her squarely. "Can I count on you?"

Kate struggled with an immediate impulse to promise Chase anything. Would she always be vulnerable to this man even though in the past he had proved he was not bound by the same principles? His code was one of his own making, and it didn't include generosity and the selflessness he was asking of her, she reminded herself. With an effort, she wrenched her gaze from the mesmerizing intensity of his, averting her face.

"I'm afraid I can't promise you that, Chase." Was that her voice sounding so confident when her heart was pounding, every nerve quaking at the step she was taking? "I won't be staying on now that Langford's is no longer a part of my family."

Heavy silence greeted her announcement, and when it lengthened uncomfortably, she finally turned to encounter Chase's grim expression, his features a frozen mask.

"You're quitting." It was not a question but a contemptuous indictment delivered with a twist of his mouth.

Mentally, Kate gathered her strength by recalling the time Chase had rejected her, had been disloyal to her father, had disapproved of her. All of the reasons she did not need to feel any sense of responsibility to the forty years of Langford tradition she had just renounced rose in her mind to justify her decision.

"I understand," she challenged, "that with your brilliant expertise, turning Langford's into a paying enterprise should be a piece of cake." Some of the bitterness in her heart spilled over into her words. "Consequently, I see no need to hide the decision I made as soon as I learned that dad had sold the business." If she had hoped Chase would believe she was giving notice of a carefully thought out decision, she was soon disillusioned.

His eyes raked her haughtily defiant features. "You mean you made the decision when you heard *whom* Phillip sold to, don't you? Let's have a little honesty between us, Kate."

It was an effort to swallow the chagrin that rose in response to Chase's perception. Trust him to see through her motives with the same shrewdness with which he had read her emotions years earlier. How did he do it? she wondered wildly.

When she didn't reply, he went on relentlessly. "I might have expected this from you. What about your professed concern for the employees who comprise Langford's, the men and women whose livelihood hinges on the success of the business? These are difficult times, as I'm sure you are aware."

She winced at the hint of sarcasm that entered his voice. Obviously, he didn't think she had suffered any deprivations. Did he still see her as Phillip Langford's spoiled, willful daughter? Chase had paused; then he resumed with slightly less antagonism, his voice taking on a coaxing quality.

"What would it cost you to stay the course for a few months if you could contribute meaningfully toward turning the business around?"

Her head bent, the fingers of one hand rubbed wearily against her temples. "Is it really necessary for me to stay on?" With a sense of surprise, she heard the beginning of her own about-face. Were all his victories so neat? In a few shrewd personal remarks, he had provoked guilt and appealed to her sense of responsibility for Langford's employees, hinting subtly at her own affluent life style, so that only a selfish worm could have held out against him.

She raised her eyes to his, expecting at the very least triumph and smug satisfaction with his easy victory; instead, she saw relief, even a sudden flash of pleasure, warming the rich brown of his eyes.

"You won't be sorry," he promised with a grin that subtracted years from his face. Kate's too ready response had her smiling in return, the contrary desire to thwart him disappearing like morning frost under sunshine.

For a moment, silence filled the room. "We'll be seeing a lot of each other, Kate," Chase began, his eyes roving the lines of her face with an indulgent tilt of his mouth. "I don't want us at each other's throats. I had hoped for a less hostile reception from you. I still don't know how we almost came to blows."

Careful, my girl, Kate warned herself. You're in danger of folding completely under the practiced charm of Chase Jamison. She drew a deep, determined breath. "If you had hoped for less hostility, then why did you say things which I was sure to resent?"

He threw her a glance over his shoulder. "You mean you resent that I was curious about your position and how you handled it?"

Kate nodded shortly. "Among other things."

He smiled tautly. "Oh, yes. I wasn't supposed to mention past indiscretions, was I?"

She held on to her temper with an effort. "No gentleman would."

He moved toward her, his eyes mocking. "But then, Kate, I'm not a gentleman, am I? My blood was never blue enough for you, was it?"

She frowned. "What's that supposed to mean?"

"Don't pretend you don't know," he challenged. "You weren't satisfied with all the proper guys at your feet. You had to single out someone who was different, didn't you?" His expression was shuttered, closed against her searching gaze. "Did you ever stop to think what might result from your selfishness?"

A part of Kate was urging her to deny his accusations, to assert how completely preposterous they were, but she couldn't articulate a word in her defense. Tears sprang to her eyes, and she moved, desperately needing to conceal from him that his words had pierced a shell of guilt that she had never been able to banish. She turned her back to him, her shoulders ramrod straight with the effort to seem indifferent.

"I think you probably got more than you bargained for that night, hmm, Kate?" Taunting, mocking, he kept prodding until Kate began to feel like a butterfly at the mercy of a cruel collector.

"I suppose I did get a bargain," she was stung into retaliating. "But what could I expect—it was hardly memorable." With an effort, she smiled coolly. "In fact, it was definitely a forgettable incident."

Her barb must have pricked his masculine pride. Kate watched as his eyes glittered with a dangerous light and his mouth firmed into a straight line.

"So it was entirely forgettable, as you recall?"

She laughed shortly. "Entirely."

Before she could sidestep, the fingers of one hand had curled around the point of her shoulder. "Then let's see if my technique has improved, shall we?"

His free hand clamped around her neck, propelling her forward and tilting her chin up so that she braced for a punishing assault from the hard male mouth descending toward hers. But the expected collision never happened. Stopping short, Chase's mouth settled onto hers gently, almost tentatively, as though savoring what was in store. In persuasive little forays along the outline of her lips, he lightly touched each corner, erotically tracing the slightly parted entrance to her mouth with his tongue. Kate's heart practically stopped, then resumed at a racing tempo.

She sensed his satisfaction, and his fingers released her chin, moving lower and spreading out to stroke the sensitive line of her throat, lingering on the wildly fluttering pulse. He nuzzled her skin, nibbling lovingly at her lips until he was satisfied that she was rendered helpless; then he enfolded her more completely into his embrace and kissed her with a smoldering passion, plundering the soft interior of her mouth hungrily, draining from her all the sweetness of her involuntary response. Kate found herself yielding to the dangerous expertise of a master of the art, for having been robbed of what resistance she would have been able to muster by the disarming tenderness of his technique, she was lost. She heard her own small sigh of pleasure with surprise and wonder unfolding in her mind.

Her hands had been imprisoned against the wall of his chest, so that had she been of a mind to resist, it would have been difficult against his superior strength. But resistance wasn't what Kate had in mind. Still in control, Chase reacted to the restive movements of her hands by lessening the pressure that held them captive so that she could free them and wrap them around his neck. She arched her body into the masculine angles of his, mindlessly accommodating so that the pleasure that exploded everywhere he touched could be prolonged.

He stopped suddenly, raising his hands to fasten around her wrists, removing her arms from their clinging possession around his neck.

"I guess my technique has improved, hmm?"

Kate could only stare, stricken and bereft now that his warmth was removed. Her emotions were so mixed that she was certain she couldn't string together enough words to express an intelligent thought.

"Speechless, too?" Chase mocked, as if he could read her mind.

Kate couldn't control the resultant emotion that spiraled instantly at his taunt. Her reaction had furnished Chase with fuel for his own private amusement for a long time, she thought, wincing with humiliation. Right now, all she wanted was to get away from him. At all cost, she mustn't let him suspect the effect he had on her.

"Please leave, Chase," she ordered in a shaken voice, hanging on to her composure by a thread, her gaze fixed on a point beyond the window. She felt his speculative stare, knew that he was assessing the effect of his kiss.

"If possible," he murmured almost to himself, "you have grown even more beautiful, Kate." He extended a hand and trailed two fingers gently down her averted cheek, laughing softly when she quickly stepped out of reach.

Kate breathed sharply, biting a lower lip that threatened to betray her. Why, oh, why had she lost control in his arms like that? He would think she was still at the mercy of her emotions, just as he remembered her at seventeen. And she wasn't.

Struggling to collect her thoughts, she turned her gaze to him, her chin tilted in a line just short of defiance. "Was there anything else?"

He regarded her steadily, his tawny eyes locked with the deep blue of hers. A hint of a smile played at the corner of his mouth.

"Well, what are you waiting for?" Her whole body quivered in fear or anticipation. Maybe hysteria, she thought wildly. "You have what you came for," she reminded him, her voice urging his departure.

He reached for the door. "Not quite." He stepped over the threshold and turned. "Not quite."

Chapter Five

Kate rushed forward as Chase disappeared through the door, and before he could pull it closed behind him, she slammed it with all her strength. She was trembling with reaction, aware at the same time of the confused muddle of her emotions. She was horrified to learn that she was still capable of responding to Chase, deeply outraged that with typical male assurance, he would dare to take liberties that other men in her life had not even attempted. Ruthlessly, she squelched the voice of reason that pointed out that she had had more than ample opportunity to stop Chase but had done nothing. In fact, he could be excused for thinking she welcomed the opportunity to be in his arms, so little resistance did she show.

She leaned against the door, her chest rising and falling in the aftermath of their confrontation, mutely acknowledging that Chase had certainly come out of it better than she had. She supposed he had simply shocked her senseless, surprising her with a complete absence of force, braced as she had been for ruthless assault. His technique had definitely improved, she thought dazed, if it had ever been lacking.

Still reeling, she moved into the sunroom, sinking into a rattan couch upholstered in lime and white. It was difficult to think coherently, but after a few minutes, she forcefully put aside the disturbing aftermath of the encounter with Chase and began to consider the situation with some measure of calm.

Her first impulse was to check the facts of Chase's claim. But no, common sense dictated that it wasn't necessary. Although she had tossed out accusations about his lack of integrity, she knew deep down that he wouldn't lie. Apparently, in all those years of dogging Chase's every step, her childish trust in him hadn't been destroyed. Besides, he knew as well as she that it was a simple matter to check the authenticity of his claim; because of that, there would be no purpose in Chase's making assertions that she could easily disprove.

So now the question was what would be the best way to cope with the situation. On Monday morning, he would no doubt turn up ready for a full day's work, and she would be expected to accommodate him if he needed her. He had accomplished what he came for, if securing her promise to stay had been his goal that morning, and with very little effort, she acknowledged ruefully. Appealed to, as Chase had so shrewdly done, she had been a pushover. What else would he demand of her, she wondered suddenly. Firmly, she thrust aside doubt that she could withstand further blandishments from Chase. She admitted he was a formidable adversary, but she would be on guard more than ever now. So with some of her confidence restored, Kate felt reasonably sure she could handle everything. What would be more difficult, she thought with a deep frown between her brows, would be arranging her personal life to accommodate Chase's actual presence in the house.

She was turning over in her mind the endless possibilities that thought evoked when she heard her grandmother and Ron returning. She rose, glancing quickly into a small bamboo-framed mirror hanging on the wall of the sunroom. Except for the heightened color of her cheeks, there was hardly any evidence of her duel with Chase. She turned to the opening door with a bright, slightly forced smile.

"Back already?"

Olivia shot a keen look into Kate's face and dropped a bag that apparently held her purchases on the coffee table in front of the couch. "As a matter of fact, we have been back for a good ten minutes, but we ran into Chase as he was preparing to drive away." She placed her handbag on the couch and then seated herself, her fingers raking through her gray hair.

Kate drew a long breath. "Well, I suppose he's told you the bad news?"

Her remark earned a frown from two quarters, and Kate braced for an attack from Ron, judging by the expression on his face.

"I don't see any of this as bad, Kate," he said with a return of puzzled interest in the glance he turned on her. "I assume you're referring to the fact that we'll have to share Fox Briar with him, but I hope you've considered just how much worse it could have been. If the buyer had been anyone besides Chase Jamison, then the thought of sharing anything with the former owners would have been laughable."

Kate had the grace to flush, but swallowing her pride was something she had very little experience in, and she was finding it almost impossible. "Of course I realize that, Ronnie," she acknowledged, "but I was stunned that Fox Briar was included in the sale of assets just like a . . . another piece of office furniture. It's going to take me a little while to accept it."

Her grandmother subjected her to a knowing look. "To accept sharing Fox Briar or to accept sharing it with Chase Jamison?"

Kate's hands curled tightly, and she felt the pressure of her nails against her palms. Apparently, Livvy had zeroed in accurately on the conflicting emotions that assailed her whenever Chase was mentioned.

"Naturally, I feel awkward having him here at Fox Briar with us, Livvy," she replied stiffly. "Don't you?"

Olivia looked perplexed. "Absolutely not," she said, her tone to Kate slightly accusing. "It's not as if he's going to be right in the house with us, Kate. I think you're showing a remarkable lack of appreciation."

Kate blinked uncomprehendingly. "But I thought he was going to be in the house. He told me—"

Ron's delighted chuckle halted her in midsentence. "Did he tell you he was moving into the main house?" His blue eyes sparkled delightedly, observing Kate's obvious confusion.

Kate's gaze swung from one to the other. "I wish someone would simply tell me what's going on!" she suddenly exploded. "If he told you something different from what he told me, I'd like to hear it."

Rising frustration sharpened Kate's voice, and Olivia came to her rescue. "Naturally, we don't know what he told you, dear, but Chase plans to live in the beach cottage. After all, there are six acres of land, and the cottage is situated at the edge of it. That's hardly an invasion of privacy." She paused significantly. "I don't want to sound like I'm preaching, Kate, but Chase does have every right to live in this house. I'm puzzled as to how he is arranging matters so that we stay and he takes that unimposing little cottage to live in." She frowned. "It's not what you'd expect from a person with his usual life style."

Kate's head was dizzy from trying to reconcile her own information and Olivia's explanation. She inhaled deeply, rubbing a forefinger against a throbbing pain between her brows. "Wait a minute, please. I seem to have missed out on something here, or I misunderstood what Chase told me only a few minutes ago. Which is it?" Her eyes flicked expectantly from her grandmother to her brother, who was obviously enjoying her discomfiture. Olivia relented first.

"Apparently, Chase saw fit to tease you a little, Kate," she began soothingly, hurrying on as she noted the spark in Kate's eyes. "You know he's been familiar with Fox Briar's grounds since he was a boy, and naturally he knew of the beach cottage. It's soundly constructed, and with a little renovating, he told us, it will satisfy his needs when he is in town."

Olivia's last phrase diverted Kate for a moment. "Is he planning on commuting?" Although the less I see of him, the better, she added silently, stoutly denying the sinking feeling that accompanied the thought that Chase was not going to be in Baytown permanently.

"It's possible, I would imagine," Olivia said. "Although I'm certainly not aware of his plans. As I mentioned before, for a man with his usual life style—"

"What is his usual life style?" Kate interrupted cynically.

Olivia's mouth firmed in exasperation. "Kate! You must know his corporation is registered in Texas. I'm only assuming he must maintain a residence there. Common sense dictates that he wouldn't need two residences which have to be maintained in the style of Fox Briar."

Kate's lips thinned. "Hardly."

Her grandmother ignored that. "I understand that there is to be no change in our circumstances. As Langfords, we will remain in this house, and we have Chase to thank for that."

It was all Kate could do to smother the avalanche of words that formed in her mind. It seemed that Olivia and Ron were perfectly comfortable with the new circumstances. They were having no difficulty accepting everything Chase said, going so far as to see the future as a rosy thing with him in charge. Nervously, she nibbled her lower lip, her thoughts taking several directions at once. It was obvious any reservations she might have concerning the future were not shared by her family. If Chase was up to something, then it would be up to her to ferret it out. No one else could be depended on to see him without rose-colored glasses. She drew a determined breath, mentally squaring her shoulders. She must not succumb to his lethal charm.

"I'm really looking forward to having Chase around," Olivia was saying, the affection she had felt for the young man clear in her voice. "He's always been one of my favorite people."

Kate swallowed an immediate negative reply. "Don't the circumstances of his leaving eight years ago cause you any hesitation?"

Now it was Olivia's turn to frown perplexedly. "Why should they? He explained it all to Phillip, and as far as I'm concerned, it's all old news." She leaned toward her granddaughter earnestly. "And Kate, I feel I must advise you to forget it, too. What possible good can come of raking up the past? It's not like you to take such an ungenerous attitude. It's distinctly unlike you."

"What do you mean, he explained it all to dad?"

Kate asked, feeling once again as though she had
missed something important but not certain when or
what.

The old lady seemed to be losing patience at last.
"Kate! Didn't you hear me earlier today?" She
turned to Ron. "Surely you recall my relating what
happened when Phillip ran into Chase in California
at that conference?" She looked irritated that the
effort she had expended had been wasted.

Ron's lips quirked as he leaned forward and
plucked an apple from a bowl of fruit on the coffee
table. "I remember, Livvy, but I think Kate was in
the kitchen. Perhaps she missed the most important
part." He directed a wicked look into her baffled
features. "Of course, she did say she didn't want to
hear Chase's name anymore today." He bit into the
apple.

"Ron! What conference? What happened in California?" In about a minute, her patience was going
to snap, and they would both get another dose of her
temper.

Ron laughingly held up two hands to ward off a
blow. "All right, all right. Livvy was saying that dad
actually met up with Chase at a shipbuilder's conference in California several years ago. Apparently,
you were in college, so maybe that's why you didn't
know anything about it. I guess dad must have
forgotten to tell you the next time you were home,
since you still seem unaware of the facts."

Kate waited, silently counting in her head, struggling to control mounting impatience. "What facts,
Ron?"

"Well"—Ron settled back, munching the apple
and warming to his topic—"Chase told dad that after
he left Langford, he was understandably sore and
bitter over the allegations against his name. First
thing he did was get himself a job with an outfit
which he later became part owner in. I believe it had

something to do with patents for new devices in yachting navigation. Anyway, as soon as he could, he began to try to figure out what had happened back at Langford, and with the help of someone he trusted back here, they finally discovered that T. J. Jacobs—remember him?" He raised both brows, and receiving a confused nod, went on. "T. J. had sold the plans to a competitor."

Kate was frowning in concentration. "I remember dad suddenly firing T. J., and he had been with the company as long as I could remember."

"It was a blow to Phillip, but he took what action he could to right a wrong," Olivia added. "As I said, I believe you were in college at that time, but my memory is a little vague."

"I was," Kate acknowledged, "but that conference was in San Francisco, and dad bought me a ticket to fly out to him and visit California at the same time. If he saw Chase, he never mentioned it to me."

Her grandmother looked mystified for a moment. "Well, that's certainly odd," she mused thoughtfully. "I wonder why Phillip failed to mention Chase to you?"

Kate wondered, too, but she said nothing. She wondered if Phillip had recalled what he had referred to as her quixotic attempt to provide Chase with an alibi for that night. If he had, maybe he thought nothing would be gained by discussing it with Kate even though he must have known she would have been keenly interested in Chase's innocence. Or maybe, to give her father the benefit of the doubt, in the busy days of the conference, it had slipped his mind. One thing was certain; she would never know now.

Later that night, in bed, her thoughts returned again to Chase and her newly discovered facts. Now his name was cleared, and her animosity toward him eight years before had been misplaced and unfair. She wished suddenly she had not revealed the reason for her dislike of Chase to Ben and Charlotte. She must correct their thinking first thing the next day. And another thing was certain; she could not deny a deep sense of relief that Chase had not used that brief, passionate encounter with her seventeen-year-old emotions to damage her family's business. Unwilling to allow her thoughts to wander any further, she concentrated on going to sleep.

A romantic ballad pierced the cocoon of intense relaxation that cradled Kate, and she opened sleepy eyes to blink at the green digital numerals on her clock radio. She reached out with a lazy, sensual grace and touched the electronic bar that turned off the music. Her hands delved into the tawny thickness of her hair, and she stretched languorously. It was a deliciously cool April morning with little humidity, just perfect for an early run. She rose up from her bed, shedding the froth of nylon that was her nightgown, and disappeared into the bathroom.

Emerging moments later, she pulled on her favorite running suit and sank onto a chair to lace and tie the comfortable sneakers, which had seen better days. The only concession to vanity that she made was to stroke a brush through her sun-streaked hair and pull it into a perky and becoming ponytail. A quick coat of lip gloss prevented her full curved lips from irritation in the salt-laden breeze that was always freshening on the Gulf.

In ten minutes, she was down on the beach, turning her face into the wind, building up speed with a pleasure that was almost sensual. On days like this, two or three times a week if she could manage it, Kate forgot everything and gave herself up to the joy of running. The bright green of her suit was the only splash of color against the buff sands and pearl-gray water along the stretch of beach that bordered Langford land. The solitude that was always hers to claim in the early morning was a strong incentive in luring her outdoors, where an affinity with the sea and gulls on the wing tugged at the deepest part of her. Sheer happiness flared in her, exploding in a wide grin that couldn't be suppressed even if it had been Kate's nature to suppress a joyful impulse.

It took her a moment to recognize the muffled sound intruding on her solitude. Chase, breathing deeply with the effort of jogging, materialized at her side, his graceful lope corresponding easily with her measured strides. She favored him with a brief glance, not according the suddenly increased tempo of her heartbeat the slightest regard.

"What are you doing here?" she panted, unfaltering in her rhythm.

"Why do you ask?" he countered, not looking at her. "Do you have some exclusive claim to the Gulf of Mexico?"

"Of course not." How did he manage to always put her on the defensive? she wondered in vexation. "I'm usually alone on the beach at this hour. I guess I was just startled." It was difficult to keep her tone indifferent, but she made an effort.

He laughed, and her eyes flew to his face as though in a reflex action. His laughter was deep and infectious, coming from the depths of his broad chest, which at this moment was heaving in a wholly masculine enjoyment of physical exertion. He wore a gray sweatshirt. The sleeves had been cut off, with the result that his powerful biceps were bare, and his arms, bent at the elbow, swung in measured rhythm with his stride. Her eyes moved of their own accord down to the athletic shorts that hugged his slim hips, and the sight of the tanned flesh of his muscular thighs and legs had her errant gaze bouncing away, but not before he had seen and been amused by her compulsive regard.

The hard line of his mouth softened, and he grinned into her flushed face, his teeth white and even, his entire appearance one of bold good health and animal maleness. He reached out a hand and caught her arm. "Let's stop a minute. You look overheated."

She yanked her arm out of his grasp, knowing the color on her face had nothing to do with the heat. "Don't grab at me like that," she snapped. "And I'm not overheated!"

Ignoring her protests, he caught her arm again and with an agile twist stopped her and pulled her down onto the sand.

"What do you think you're doing?" she demanded, struggling to loosen his hold on her arm, her feet going out from under her even as she tugged ineffectively to retain her balance.

"I'm taking a break, and you can keep me company," he said, a mischievous look in his eyes. Then, spotting something in the distance, he let her get up. "Let's go over to that tree."

He stood, and with both hands under her arms, palms flat and warm against her rib cage, he lifted her and hauled her unceremoniously the few dozen feet to a lone tree that had managed to withstand the ravages of incessant wind and occasional hurricanes for at least fifty years. A deck surface had been constructed at the base of the tree years before on the instructions of her father. Kate and Ron had spent many hours there, and sometimes Chase had been with them. Some instinct warned her against sitting there again with Chase, but her protests were ignored. He deposited her carelessly onto the deck and then joined her.

"Now isn't this nice?" he teased, turning his face into the breeze, by all intents savoring the feel of the early-morning freshness against his body. Close to him, Kate could feel the heat emanating from him, and she shivered in response to his earthy magnetism.

She forced herself to recall his highhandedness in waylaying her and dragging her against her will to this wretched bench, but it was difficult. She was torn between righteous indignation and an absurd desire to spend some time in his company. She slanted him an assessing glance from beneath her long lashes.

"What are you up to, Chase?" she asked before she could stop herself.

He turned lazily inquiring eyes upon her. "Why do I have to be up to anything?"

She curbed the urge to hit him. "You know what I mean. Why did you drag me over here? You knew I wasn't tired. I could run five miles without tiring, and I'll bet you know it."

His mouth quirked with amusement. "How could I know that?"

She jerked her shoulders with impatience. "You have your ways. You seem to know everything else." Somehow the conversation was beyond her control again, and she looked around unseeingly, impotently clenching her teeth. "You moved in and invaded my home, you will invade my office tomorrow morning, and even Livvy and Ron have succumbed to your charm." She turned her turbulent gaze accusingly on him. "I'm not the inexperienced teenager I was when you last knew me, Chase. You can just remember that, whatever your plans are."

A tiny muscle moved in his jaw as his eyes roved freely over her angry face. "You make me sound like a dangerous menace, but I don't think you have to worry. With your suspicions alerted, I can hardly get away with anything."

She eyed him warily. He was laughing at her, the

beast! And he was a dangerous menace. She wasn't certain just exactly how he posed a danger to her, but he did.

"Why did you allow me to think you were occupying the main house at Fox Briar?"

He shrugged nonchalantly. "Why not? You obviously expected no mercy from the thief and traitor you accused me of being."

"And that's another thing," she said, his attitude fueling her indignation. "How could I have known the hydroplane plans had been taken by T. J.? Dad never mentioned it, and I assumed it was still an unsolved mystery."

"If you were interested, you could have asked eight years ago." His eyes studied her coolly. "Why didn't you ask, Kate? Surely there was some natural curiosity on your part. After all, you played a major part in the events of that night."

"I thought you meant to use the time we spent together that night as an alibi. When you didn't, I . . . I had no choice but to think you had taken the plans." Why did she feel so guilty furnishing him her reasons for not coming to him and openly asking for an explanation?

"Even after the years you had known me, you could still believe something like that?" His mouth thinned with disbelief.

"It's true," she asserted, strangely unwilling to have him misunderstand her feelings. "You have to understand, Chase. I had just seen a part of you . . . I mean that night you acted completely out of character as far as I was concerned. I figured there could easily be more about you that I didn't know."

He turned a brooding stare out toward the Gulf. "I guess you were younger even than I thought."

"What do you mean?"

"I suppose you thought that with my background I could hardly possess any integrity. Isn't that right?"

She was stunned to hear him express so ridiculous a remark. No one knew very much about Chase's background; just that he and his mother lived alone. There was no Mr. Jamison, but Chase had adored his mother. It was apparent in the way he spoke her name. She remembered once when he had revealed fierce resentment that his mother had been forced to work long hours, giving Kate a glimpse of a strong, protective instinct. It had endeared him to her, adding to her already strongly developing love for him. On the other hand, Kate had been indulged with every luxury a child might desire. Everything except a mother, that is. Phillip's wife had callously walked out when Kate and Ron were still toddlers, never adjusting to life in a small Gulf Coast town. Kate heard from her infrequently somewhere in Massachusetts. She had often envied Chase's warm, loving relationship with his mother.

"Why do you always bring up your background?" she asked now. "I never thought anything about that. If anything, I admired your ability to achieve success against strong odds." Her blue gaze searched his closed features, but nothing in the strongly carved profile furnished a clue to his thoughts.

"Why do you believe I'm here to do you or your family some harm?" he questioned, flicking her a sharp glance.

Kate's eyes fell uncertainly. "I don't know," she said, then adding with more assurance, "but you've only been back a few days. It's too early for me to figure out your motives."

Suddenly, he grinned, his good humor returning. "Take your time, sweetheart."

Her heart did a somersault, and she jumped up, but his arm sliced out to enclose her wrist in steel strong fingers. "Wait a minute. I'm not ready to take off yet. I'm not cooled off."

She looked into his face, tanned, rough-hewn, the

planes and angles gleaming with sweat. Her eyes wandered upward to the band that he had tied around his umber-toned hair, her glance touching on the curled tendrils around his temples and ears and onto the trickles of perspiration that rolled leisurely down his throat. She looked away uncomfortably.

"You need a towel," she muttered stiffly. "Here." She pulled a small white towel from a front pocket of her shirt, and he took it with a mocking gratitude and wiped his face and neck. Then, in one sweeping motion, he pulled his shirt over his head, shedding with his shirt, Kate's shocked imagination thought, what remained of a civilized veneer. What was left was a nearly naked giant of a man, his skin teak brown from hours in the subtropical sun, muscles in the prime of condition and shaped with the grace and sheer male beauty of a pagan god.

Kate couldn't restrain the tiny sound that escaped her lips, and to avoid having him read the expression on her face, she turned away, catching her lip between her teeth, wishing she had not come out that morning. How had she landed in this situation, before the sun was even up, she wondered hysterically.

"What's the matter, Kate?" Chase's voice mocked her, his mouth so close to her ear that she felt the whisper of his breath against the loose tendrils of her hair, which had escaped the ribbon. "You act like you've never seen a man without his shirt on"—his mouth lowered to the sensitive area between her neck and shoulder—"or is it that you prefer the cloak of night?" His voice hardened. "Is an open beach an offense to your cultured sensibilities?"

She turned, her lips parted to deliver a scorching denial, encountering instead the heat of his body close to hers. She hesitated weakly, her eyes noting the mat of chest hair curling damply, the musky male scent of his skin surging up to cloud her senses and rob her mind of the anger his words prompted. Her hand reached out of its own volition and pushed him away before he could see just how affected she was by being so close to him. Wouldn't he enjoy knowing that he put ideas into her head that were completely foreign to her nature. At least she had always thought herself capable of maintaining a disciplined control over her sexuality.

"Are you already moved into the beach house?" she said, frantically searching for some topic to break the sensual charge that crackled around them.

"Not completely," he replied, the rich warm brown of his eyes ranging lazily over the delicate lines of her face, lingering on her mouth. "I can make do with what's there for the time being. There's lots of time." He reached up and tugged the ribbon that held her ponytail, and her hair cascaded down her back and shoulders in a tawny mane. Chase lifted his gaze to hers, and all will to resist left her. Her lashes fluttered down in mute surrender, and he bent to her lips, taking them in a sweet, searching kiss. His hands were buried in her hair, molding the shape of her head so that he could taste the essence of her with ease.

Sensing his advantage, Chase moved with consummate skill to draw her against his chest, one hand pressing the small of her back and the other slipping under the confines of her shirt and sliding warmly, confidently up to her breast.

All thought was suspended in Kate's head as she savored the pleasure following in the wake of his mouth and hands. Her arms slipped around his neck, the action lifting her breasts taut with desire against the solid wall of his chest. She felt the surging response of his need while the pressure of his hands increased. When he encountered the delicate lace of her bra, he made an impatient sound in his throat, not releasing her mouth, but expertly locating the front fastener, freeing the weight of her breasts to his questing hand. Kate was floating in mindless pleasure. It permeated her senses, filling her with a sweet delight. Eagerly compliant, she allowed him to ease her down onto the deck, pushing up the soft cotton folds of her shirt. The cool rush of the Gulf breeze on her heated skin was a delicious sensation, heightening the kaleidoscope of feeling that held her captive. All sensation except Chase's touch was only background impressions, vague and insubstantial against the sheer bliss of his lovemaking.

His weight was satisfyingly heavy on her, and he lowered his mouth to the deep cleft of her breasts, burying his face in the scented flesh, his hands under her rib cage, arching her body, although there was no need, so eagerly did she respond to every sensual signal. When his lips closed on one taut peak, she gasped with the flare of pleasure that shot through her, lifting languorous arms to clasp his head, bringing it firmly against her in a mindless need, seeking a relief to the ache that claimed her. She shuddered with every stroke of his tongue, every graze of his lips, as they explored the soft feminine curves and peaks, exploding into a rapture as old as time.

Chase groaned, moving his head negatively against her, his arms tightly encircling. "I don't want to stop now," he muttered thickly, his words sounding a warning to penetrate the mists of enchantment where Kate floated. Even as he spoke, she was aware of a gradual lessening of tension in the lithely muscled frame that rested with hard satisfaction against her accommodating femininity. Her eyes fluttered open, ready to object, but his lips were still, his hands quiescent, and only the thudding of his heart, racing in a rhythm that matched her own, betrayed the effort it required to withdraw from her.

He rolled slightly sideways, taking his weight from her. She stared blankly into his eyes, seeing a blazing desire that rocked her senses. Why had he stopped? Her limbs, languorous and weighted by the passion they had shared, refused to respond as she moved weakly, her brain only just beginning to function. He reached out a tanned hand and pushed a strand of her hair away from her cheek, grazing hard knuckles against her soft skin. "How can you be so beautiful so early in the morning?" he murmured, his eyes darkened with wonder. There was smoldering fire in the gaze he slid over her vulnerable features.

Regret flickered in his eyes as he watched returning sanity banish the love-softened look of her face. "Someone's coming."

Alarm flared in the quick glance she sent toward the deserted beach.

"No, over there." Chase's eyes moved in a direction behind her, and Kate watched the slow progress of two young boys romping with a dog at the edge of the tide. His broad shoulders moved in a protective tactic, and she felt hot, betraying color surge into her face. It was just now dawning on her how completely oblivious to the world she had been in Chase's arms.

She jerked upright, pulling awkwardly at her shirt, thankful at least for the shield of his muscular frame from the curious eyes of the boys.

"Is this how you plan to while away your leisure hours, Chase?" she asked bitterly, her lips stiff with the effort it took to keep them steady.

He thrust a heavy hand through the dark thickness of his hair. "You know I didn't plan this, Kate. It just happened." He watched her as she turned jeeringly skeptical eyes away from him to gaze over the calm surface of the Gulf, sparkling with early sunshine. "I didn't exactly use force."

She jumped up, her emotions a tangle of guilt and anger and frustrated desire. She was frightened by the depth of feeling triggered by his lovemaking. "I want you to leave me alone, Chase, and I mean it! For some reason, you have decided you want Langford Marine and Fox Briar, but you'll never have me!"

Chase rose from the deck, his muscled body glazed by the morning sun. Kate passed a nervously moist tongue over her swollen lips. He was angry, her hastily flung words apparently flicking a nerve.

He leaned over and casually picked up his shirt, pulling it over his head and settling it around his tapered waistline. Turning, he studied her, a complacency in his look that had her shifting uneasily.

"Never is a long time."

Chapter Six

"Well, today's the day." Ron guided the racy silver-gray sports car through the gates of Langford Marine, maneuvering through a maze of other more modest automobiles to a reserved parking slot, and stopped with a flourish.

From the passenger's seat, Kate watched her brother with a wryly affectionate smile. Ron's taste in cars was a family joke. He insisted on driving her to work every now and then just to remind her how boring her small compact car was, and that day it had suited her to ride with Ron. Probably it had something to do with moral support, a little voice insisted, but it seemed desirable to arrive this morning reinforced by her brother's casual but full-blooded Langford presence. No one could ever say that Ron gave any more than minimum dedication to the business, but he was a Langford, and that counted this morning.

"Your opinion concerning the company's new

management is obvious, Ron," Kate observed ruefully. "I can't remember when you've popped out of
bed with such gusto on a Monday." She tilted her
head sideways, a playful smile tugging the corners of
her mouth. "As a matter of fact, it's safe to say I've
never seen you so enthusiastic Monday or any other
day of the week."

He grinned unrepentantly. "I won't deny a tiny
feeling of relief that Chase Jamison will have to
figure out how to stretch the profits to include all
that new equipment the shop superintendent is
yelling for."

Kate's smile slipped slightly at the mention of
Chase's name. She had consciously avoided thinking
of him this morning, although she had not been so
successful the previous night. After their early-
morning encounter on the beach, he had filled her
thoughts to the exclusion of all else, although she
tried to direct her mind elsewhere. It hadn't been
easy, and she had finally been reduced to calling
Charlotte Scott and inviting her over for a game of
tennis. Ben almost always spent Sunday afternoons
on the golf course, and Charlotte was not partial to
the game. She and Kate often enjoyed a few hours
together, and she was cheerful, diverting company.
Besides, Kate needed to grab the first opportunity to
retract most of what she had confided to Ben and
Charlotte about Chase. It had been a foolish impulse
in the first place, she chided herself, and she could
only explain her uncharacteristic indiscretion by the
fact that she had been thoroughly alarmed to hear
his name dropped into the conversation when she
hadn't been expecting it. Now all she wanted to do
was to get on with her work and see as little of Chase
Jamison as possible; with any kind of luck, he would
want to avoid her, too. Somehow her job seemed the
last area of her life he had not completely invaded.

"I have a huge backlog of work accumulated on

my desk," she said, forcing her thoughts into a more comfortable vein.

Ron's absent response indicated his usual tepid interest in the family business, and Kate was glad to allow her mind to move ahead to the work waiting for her. A mental list of outstanding projects was already forming in her head, her mind fastening on the details that would consume her energy for the next eight or ten hours.

Idly, she voiced one of the problems. "As for Jim Nichols' requests to upgrade that machinery, Ron, we must find the financing. It's a critical issue, because we certainly can't bid on any new construction with unreliable equipment." There was no reply from Ron, but she hadn't expected any, using her brother as a sounding board only. She opened the car door and managed to get out of the low-slung sports car with feminine grace, her thoughts still on the company's tight financial position. When her eyes raised and collided with Chase's warm brown gaze, she couldn't prevent the tiny shock that jolted her heart.

"Morning," he greeted with a tilt of his head, the mahogany brown of his hair shot through with gold glints in the morning sun.

Kate's eyes took in at a glance the subdued gray of his expensively tailored suit, lingering on the startling contrast of his tanned skin and the crisp white shirt with matching tie, then glancing off the slanted line of his mouth. Everything about him proclaimed his status as a successful, forceful businessman, but Kate could not prevent the involuntary thought as she surveyed his tall frame that his clothes merely provided a veneer of sophistication. Her senses sharpened as she recalled his appearance on the beach the day before. Underneath the veneer was an earthy, ruthlessly aggressive individual, and she reminded herself that she had better not forget it.

"Good morning, Chase," she returned coolly. At least there she was confident she would be able to hold her own. Surrounded by the work she enjoyed, employees whose respect she had worked for and valued, she could meet Chase on equal footing. The thought gave her an added confidence, helping her to master an immediate tendency to blush as she recalled their intimacy the previous day. Her chin tilted just a bit, which caused an answering glint in his assessing gaze.

"Armored for battle, I see," he remarked with an arched brow in her direction.

She frowned. "What does that mean?"

He bent to his own car and drew out a briefcase and several other folders, taking his time. She smothered an impatient sigh, torn between exploring his cryptic remark and seeking the refuge of her office.

Chase straightened, subjecting her to a comprehensive study that unnerved her even as she countered it with what she hoped looked like polite inquiry.

"Isn't that shade of gray called gun-metal?" A devilish gleam in his eyes belied the bland look on his face.

Involuntarily, Kate's gaze dropped to examine her dress. It was a crisp gray cotton with long sleeves and white Peter Pan collar and cuffs. A soft silk tie at the throat was shot with shades of white and gray and melon. The skirt was straight, defining the subtle curves of her hips and thighs, giving a tantalizing glimpse of her long, perfectly proportioned legs when she walked.

"This dress is perfectly appropriate in a business office," she declared, recalling the half-dozen other choices she had discarded that morning before her mirror. She had finally settled on this one, counting on its chaste, restrained design to create an impression of professionalism and maturity. It seemed imperative to counteract the impression he must have gotten the day before.

"Well," she demanded, goaded by his nonchalance.

"I'm pleased that you remember this is a business office," Chase stated. "I don't want Langford's to become a battleground. We both have too much to lose."

"I have no intention of fighting with you, Chase," she denied in a frosty voice, hoping for once to have the last word. She slammed the car door with finality, pivoting toward the entrance to the main building.

"That's good news," he returned, unscathed, leaning around her with a grin to push open the double doors. As she passed him, he spoke, leaning so close that the hair near her ear stirred, sending a tingle over her flesh. "Has anyone told you how beautiful you look this morning?"

Kate inhaled sharply, helpless against the sudden rush of emotion his words evoked. But she determined not to give him the satisfaction of seeing her response.

She swept ahead of him toward the haven of her office but was halted short of her goal when good manners dictated that she should wait and acknowledge the stream of enthusiastic greetings that were directed toward Chase by Langford employees who had known him years before. Even Naomi Chapman, Kate's own secretary, seemed delighted to welcome Chase, whose response was equally warm, his charm a natural thing, leaving only a skeptical Kate to raise a derisive brow. After a moment, he met her hard blue gaze, a sardonic lift of his brow the only indication that he had noticed her cynical response. Even Ron seemed eager to hand over the reins to this . . . this interloper. Her teeth snapped together, and Kate turned on her heel and disappeared into her own office, just barely restraining a childish urge to slam it.

Naomi followed a second afterward, her frizzy gray hair in its usual disarray but the bright button-black eyes as alert as ever to Kate's mood.

"Well, we should see some interesting action now," she commented with the familiarity of friendship and long association.

Kate sank into her chair and pulled a stack of papers in front of her. "That seems to be the general consensus," she replied shortly, reaching for a desk calculator and flipping the switch that turned it on. "I'm going to run this column of figures on the Wainwright estimate, Naomi. I can't quite believe the total I got when I last looked at this account."

Kate felt the studied gaze of her secretary and chanced a quick look. Naomi was regarding her with an intentness that Kate recognized and dreaded. The woman was at least twenty years her senior, and their working relationship was based on mutual respect and affection. Naomi would not hesitate to express an opinion on either Kate's professional affairs or her personal life. As a result, her next remark was not surprising.

"Do I detect a lack of enthusiasm for our new manager?" Naomi queried with a keen look into Kate's set face.

"I wouldn't say that exactly," Kate replied, punching a series of numbers into the calculator.

"What would you say exactly?" Naomi persisted. "This may be a bad pun, but we have been rudderless here at Langford Marine for the past few weeks, and Chase Jamison is a captain among men."

Kate's pencil landed on her desk with a sharp crack. "Oh, come on, Naomi, not you, too! I think I've had about all I can take of Chase Jamison's virtues. For heaven's sake! The man's only human, but to hear the accolades mouthed to him by just about everyone I've been around the last few days, you would think he was Superman."

She raked irritated fingers through her hair, heedless of the casually elegant hair style so painstakingly arranged that morning, and stood up to peer out of the window. "Were we in such bad shape around here that Chase's appearance warrants the gushing welcome he has received? How can I feel grateful that he condescended to buy Langford and everything that goes with it?" If Naomi noticed the bitterness lurking behind Kate's words, she gave no indication.

"I don't think Chase has behaved condescendingly at all, Kate," she offered with more sympathy. "I believe you're interpreting the natural pleasure which some of us have displayed at Chase's return as a kind of criticism of your father and his management, but it's not so. Everyone here thought of your father as one of the finest men who ever lived. We were lucky to work for him, and I think he knew that we felt that way, and it probably added to his responsibilities."

Kate's gaze softened, and she moved back to her chair, sinking into it wearily. She smiled a little tremulously. "I tell myself that, Naomi, but it's difficult. I don't believe some of the things I've said and done lately." She leaned her head onto her hand and rubbed her temple, a mixture of bewilderment and impatience on her expressive face.

Bright brown eyes sparked with a return of good humor. "What you need is something more than this job to concentrate on," she said, launching into a favorite theme, and Kate's sense of humor began to revive in spite of herself. Resigning herself, she leaned back, patiently prepared to hear Naomi out.

"You think this company can't run without you, Kate, and you've made your job the most important thing in your life." She hitched her chair forward confidently. "You need a real man, honey," she said, hastening on when Kate's eyes rolled heavenward. "A forceful, dynamic man, someone who can stand up to you. The trouble is that you make mincemeat out of most of the men you've known up to now," she observed knowledgeably.

"Thanks a lot." Kate's mouth twitched expressively.

Undeterred, Naomi's eyes gleamed slyly. "I've got a feeling the time is right for a change."

There was wry amusement in Kate's sudden laugh. Obviously, Naomi planned to do a little matchmaking, with Chase as the unwary quarry. She opened her mouth to nip firmly in the bud any such intention when Chase stuck his head around the door. She faltered in midthought, irritated to feel a rush of color to her cheeks.

"Is this joke private, or can anyone share it?" The full battery of his charm was behind the smile Chase divided equally between the two women. Naomi rose to leave, looking as if butter wouldn't melt.

"Oh, it's nothing, Mr. Jamison. Just a little suggestion of mine which Kate persists in resisting." She threw her employer a demure look as she disappeared through the door, and Kate bit her lip, torn between amusement and annoyance. Naomi really was the limit. She wouldn't put it past her to tell Chase just what it was she suggested to Kate.

Chase closed the door and moved toward her, the faint humor that had lingered about his firm mouth fading as he drew up to her desk.

Kate stood, needing the extra height for added courage in dealing with him. He looked so formidable standing there, all cool competence and raw aggression. Fleetingly, she observed mentally that Naomi's assessment of this man's character was right on target.

"Can I do something for you?"

A hooded expression in his eyes brought out all her wary instincts, but he nodded with a slight lessening of the straight line of his mouth. "Just a few things I wanted to mention, and it hasn't taken me long to discover that the person with the answers is Kate Langford." He was folding his long frame into a leather armchair opposite her desk as he spoke.

Kate didn't make the mistake of interpreting his statement as a compliment. Warily, she resumed her seat, schooling her expression to show only polite patience, and waited for him to continue.

Chase acknowledged her restraint with a raised brow. "I find neither you nor Ron listed on the board of directors of Langford's, Kate. Since it was a family corporation, I wondered about that."

She did not know what she had expected, but it certainly wasn't anything near the subject Chase raised. Her glance, which had been cool and unforthcoming, faltered under his keenly piercing look.

"I can't imagine why you are concerned with something which is surely a personal matter," she replied stiffly, resenting the necessity to answer questions that were none of his business. "But I believe my father felt we were too young. At least we hadn't discussed the matter for a couple of years, only when I first graduated from college. Naturally, I would be expected to become familiarized with all facets of the business. It would hardly have been appropriate otherwise."

She knew her reply sounded nebulous, but she was searching for words that would satisfy the incisive brain that she knew was weighing carefully what he heard. "That is why I was not appointed, I believe. As for Ron—"

Chase shifted his large frame in the chair, crossing

one long leg over a muscular thigh and resting a lean hand on his ankle. "I know why Ron wasn't appointed. He has absolutely no interest in entering into any decision making, and your father was sympathetic to his feelings."

A militant sparkle entered Kate's eyes. "If you're suggesting Ron was incompetent in the position—"

"I'm suggesting no such thing. Ron is competent to do anything he wishes. He simply doesn't want to use his talents at Langford's." He swept aside her anger like so much chaff in the wind, and Kate felt an impotence beginning to build up inside. This was what always happened when she and Chase were together. She lost her temper, and he remained relentlessly calm and collected. This time was going to be different. She clamped her lips together and waited.

There was an assessing quality to his look, and she found it nearly as disconcerting as his silence.

"What is it?" she demanded uncomfortably.

"I'm wondering just what your feelings are about the fact that you weren't appointed to the board."

She picked up a silver pen and made a few meaningless lines on the pad in front of her. "I think eventually I would have been appointed. It takes time, you know." Actually, Kate believed nothing of the kind. Hell would probably have frozen over before the ultraconservative members of the board would have admitted a young woman to their midst. She darted a quick look into his face but could determine nothing from the professional mask he had assumed since beginning the conversation.

"How much time?" he countered. "As it is, you're practically running the business."

He had, after only two hours on the job, put his finger precisely on one painful aspect of her work that she had long recognized but had had little success in accepting. She was often frustrated and indignant that there was so little recognition accorded her for the vital position she handled. Now that Chase was aware of the facts, he would probably enjoy the prospect of watching her yearn for something that would now be forever out of her reach.

Mercifully, he seemed to tire of the subject and was moving on to another topic. Still, he had seen her vulnerability, and every small thing he could learn about her made him more dangerous. Having him and his keen perception around was going to be a strain.

"How long has Ben Scott been with Langford's?" He shot a discreet look at his watch, and her mouth thinned.

"Ben has been here about three years. He's extremely talented, and we're very lucky to have him," she said with an edge to her words. If he thought to start cutting personnel and planned to begin with Ben, she would fight it with every weapon she could think of, Kate resolved fiercely.

"I know that," he said calmly, confounding her. "I've spent an hour with him, and he knows his numbers. He's a very good bean counter."

The term brought a glint of humor to her eyes, and her gaze, darting quickly to his, was caught and held while they shared an instant's rapport. For a moment, she was reminded of their long-ago affinity for appreciating the humor in the most unlikely moments.

"Accounting comes naturally to Ben," she volunteered, wrenching her thoughts back in line. "I rely on him to keep me within budget." Soon enough he would find out that between them she and Ben just barely managed to juggle the assets so that no catastrophe had yet occurred. But they both were aware that things were shaky, especially in the last eighteen months. She supposed Chase's methods would have wrung that information from Ben within a very short time.

"I'm happy you recognized his talent so soon," she stated with satisfaction. "Ben and Charlotte—"

"Are your friends, I know," he finished dryly. "Do you spend a lot of time in New Orleans?"

She blinked at the unexpected question. Apparently, he was referring to the Mardi Gras ball. "No, not really. I like a lot of things about New Orleans, but I only go occasionally."

"Like when you want to see Mark Devereaux?"

The tenuous hold she had kept on her temper snapped. "What does this have to do with anything?" she demanded, jumping to her feet and eying him balefully.

He thrust his chair back, coming to his feet in one fluid movement. "Who else are you involved with?"

With a sharp pivot, she left her desk and strode to the door. As her hand closed on the knob, Chase caught her, his hard fingers closing on the soft flesh of her upper arm.

"Look, maybe I shouldn't—"

She raised indigo-dark eyes to meet his, breathing hard. "Maybe you shouldn't!" she repeated, incensed. "You're darn right you shouldn't! You have no right questioning me about my private life. You came in here to discuss business with me. This is my office, and I demand you leave if you can't confine your remarks to matters pertaining to the company."

There was plenty more she wanted to say, but she was interrupted by the buzz of her intercom. She pushed the button impatiently, her eyes flashing angrily. "What is it?" The moment's pause before her secretary spoke revealed Naomi's surprise at the unaccustomed brusqueness in Kate's voice.

"Mark Devereaux is calling, Kate. Shall I take a message?"

Such a coincidence was almost comical, although Kate was in no mood to see humor in anything. "No, thanks, Naomi," she said with a return of her usual cordiality. "You know I always take Mark's calls." Let Chase chew on that, she thought defiantly, lifting the receiver and greeting Mark with a husky warmth that took him completely by surprise and drew an expression of disgust from Chase.

"Sweetheart, I'm going to be in Baytown tomorrow. How about dinner?"

She allowed a look of pleasure to steal across her face, her gaze centering on a point just left of Chase's jaw that was clenched into an uncompromising angle. "That sounds delightful," she gushed, disgusting even herself. "What time?"

She jotted the time on her calendar, and as Mark continued chatting, absently traced a pattern of lines and squares. Her pen moved languidly even as her husky responses to Mark's conversation prolonged what would normally have been a two-minute exchange.

She glanced up as Chase made an impatient sound, and with feigned reluctance, terminated the call, leaving a very pleased, although somewhat puzzled, Mark on the other end.

Kate rose, determined to usher him out no matter how strange it would look to Naomi and whoever else might happen to witness the great Chase Jamison being thrown out of her office. Anticipating her intention, Chase leaned against the door, preventing her from opening it. As they faced each other, she was conscious of the power and force of him, her eyes picking out individual characteristics in his face—the rugged line of his jaw, those sherry-brown eyes, hooded now as he contemplated her own flushed face. What was he thinking? she wondered, her senses sidetracked by the musky male scent of his aftershave.

Almost as if he read the betraying conflict within, she saw his eyes darken with a sensual awareness, and she stepped back warily.

"Relax," he ordered. "I was out of line. If you choose Devereaux as a consort, who am I to question your taste?" There was mocking disdain in his words, concealing nothing of his opinion of Mark. His apology did nothing to appease her anger, but reluctantly she watched him return to his chair; then she returned and sank guardedly into her own. Obviously, he had not finished, and her curiosity won out over her indignation.

"There are a couple of other matters which I'm sure you have information on," he stated, his manner reverting adroitly to business.

After a moment, Kate managed to submerge the clamor of her temper, pushing into the background the righteously indignant anger Chase's words had precipitated. She suspected she would be required to exercise more discipline in dealing with this maddening man than she had ever known she possessed.

By the time Chase had finished, she was once again composed. Only when he had departed did she collapse like a doll whose stuffing was removed. Yes, it was going to be a strain working all day long with the new manager.

After lunch, as she was finishing a quick sandwich at her desk, the intercom on her telephone buzzed.

"Yes, this is K—"

"Come in here, Kate," came the curt command.

She replaced the receiver with a crash. Common courtesy obviously was going to be more than she could expect from the new manager, she supposed. She tidied the top of her desk, then drew out lipstick and comb from her purse and repaired her makeup. Taking her time, she looked critically at her reflection in the mirror, eying the smooth texture of her tawny hair, flicking the ends with a careless expertise, ignoring a second strident buzz of her intercom. She replaced her purse, picked up a note pad and pen and strolled out.

As she entered his office, Chase looked up, a tense irritation lending a fierceness to his gaze. "Would you tell me what the hell this is," he ordered, shoving a paper across his desk. "I can't believe what I'm reading."

She picked up the papers and settled into a cushioned sofa that her father had chosen for his office. Deliberately closing out the disturbing picture of Chase, impatiently expectant, she scanned the first few lines.

"This is the Roberts contract," she began with more assurance than she actually felt. "What is it you don't understand?"

He rubbed an irritated hand abruptly around the back of his neck, exhaling sharply. "I understand, but what I want to know is, how did it happen?"

Warily, she held his gaze. "How did what happen?"

He stood suddenly, both palms flat on the top of the desk. "You know what I'm talking about, Kate. That's a bid for a tugboat, and the cost estimates are about twenty-five percent less than they should be. We'll lose our shirts if we honor a ridiculous contract such as this one," he informed her grimly.

Kate paused, the logic of his argument well known to her. "Have you talked to Ben?"

He nodded shortly. "Briefly. Ben assured me the contract is a document which Phillip planned to honor." He lifted the receiver of the desk phone and stabbed the push buttons with barely suppressed violence. "Ben, come in here!"

Kate crossed her slim legs, easing back against the sofa, deliberately ignoring the interest that quickened momentarily in Chase's eyes when his gaze was drawn to the shapely curve of her ankles. Neither spoke as they waited like suspended antagonists for the appearance of Ben Scott.

"You wanted to see me, Chase?" His friendly face reflected nothing more than polite inquiry as he waited for Chase's reply, and Kate was forced to conclude that Ben was already comfortable with the new manager. Apparently, he was satisfied to transfer loyalties to Chase Jamison without a second thought.

"Kate and I were discussing the Roberts contract," Chase began with weary patience. "She seems to believe you can shed some more light on what I think is an incredibly foolish bid."

Ben looked quickly at Kate, who was peering fixedly at the note pad on her knee. "Well, Kate and I have had some conversation about that particular contract, Chase," Ben began tentatively, his gaze centered on Kate's bent head. "It was ordered by Gus Roberts," he said, stating an obvious fact.

Chase's smothered oath was not lost on either of them. "I know the principal is Gus Roberts," he grated, hanging on to his temper with difficulty. "What I want is an explanation for the bottom line. You must have compiled the figures, Ben. Why did Gus get a low quote like this?"

Ben's glance at Kate was at once apologetic and resigned. He laughed shortly, pushing his glasses more securely into place, a gesture that Kate knew signified uncertainty.

"I will explain, Ben," she said, standing and directing her dark blue gaze into Chase's hard face, his look clearly indicating he expected some kind of explanation. "Dad knew the price was too low when he quoted it to Gus, but Gus's business is going through a low right now. If he didn't get the new tug, he would certainly go under. Langford's agreed to build it for him at that price."

Chase's expression was unreadable as he watched her. Kate's ready temper was simmering, the necessity of making the explanation causing her to meet his eyes defiantly. Chase noted all the signals with a twitch of his sensual lips, completely confusing her.

"So now I find Phillip operating a thriving charity in addition to the other questionable practices I've discovered today." He shook his dark brown head in silent amazement. "No wonder he wanted to chuck it all and—"

Kate's gaze sharpened. Was there something else that Chase was aware of and she didn't know? He seemed in possession of an amazing range of facts about the business, which was unusual, considering he had only been in the office one day. Had Chase and her father discussed the business on more than a strictly buyer-seller basis?

Ben sank down onto the sofa. "I don't want this to sound disloyal to Phillip," he began with an appealing look in Kate's direction, "but Kate did try to reason with Phillip on the Gus Roberts thing. She argued for days after we compiled the bid package that we couldn't afford to do business that way. Phillip just wouldn't be reasonable. He knew Gus needed the tug and if he didn't get it, Gus would be out of business within a year. So we began construction." He drew a resigned sigh. "Jim Nichols, the shop superintendent, can give you a progress report on the job, Chase. He's having some difficulty because he needs new equipment in the shop."

Kate and Ben watched as Chase dropped into the leather upholstered chair that had belonged to Phillip Langford. He placed both hands on the desk, splaying them out and studying them for a long moment. He glanced up and met the wary faces across his desk and smiled, one corner of his mouth slightly crooked, lending the smile a rakishness that caught at Kate's breath. "Look's like we've got our work cut out for us, folks."

Kate blinked, resisting the incredible weakness that spread into her veins, recognizing the familiar malady as one that Chase evoked in her years earlier and that apparently she had never overcome. She was still highly susceptible to this man. Instead of the critical attack that she was braced for, he had merely absorbed the facts and accepted the challenge they presented. The mature Chase Jamison was going to be a formidable foe indeed. She refused to acknowledge the sane inner voice that urged caution in dealing with him. She could handle whatever he dished out.

Chapter Seven

Six weeks later, Kate was feeling less confident. At first, she had gone to some pains to maintain a polite, cool distance when she had to deal with Chase. She had determined that the only way she could ever hope to work with him would be if she let him know at the outset that any sexual advances would not be tolerated. The trouble was, he hadn't really approached her since that morning, and his behavior during the day at the office was proper almost to the point of indifference. Only rarely did she catch him watching her with what could be interpreted as a glimmer of male interest. Except for their occasional skirmishes at the office when they differed on some technical issue, Chase treated her with the same easy friendliness with which he treated everyone. Kate was nursing a perverse reaction— relief that she wouldn't have to fend off any more of his advances and pique that he didn't find her desirable enough at least to give it a try.

Caught up in her thoughts of Chase—thoughts that plagued her all too frequently these days—Kate barely spared a glance for the passing landscape as she guided her car off the beach road into the driveway that led to Fox Briar. It was a blissfully cool April day. High cumulous clouds in a brilliant cerulean sky occasionally blocked the otherwise-fierce rays of the southern sun. She slid her fingers under her hair, lifting the heavy mass from her neck. The breeze felt deliciously sensuous, she mused, reminded of the feel of Chase's mouth against her skin. Abruptly, she checked the rush of sensation that the thought provoked.

It was not the first time she was conscious of a vague restlessness pervading what had been the even tenor of her life. And it took no great wisdom to trace her dissatisfaction to a preoccupation with thoughts of Chase Jamison. Kate no longer tried to deny to herself that he was the most attractive man she had ever known. He had been when she was seventeen, and he was now. And though she tried to convince herself that she could resist his appeal, an incident a few days earlier had destroyed that myth.

Somehow she had not allowed herself to think of Chase's life before he returned to Baytown. Considering her own response to him, it seemed incredible that she had been unprepared for the appearance of his mistress.

She and Chase and Ben had been engaged in a discussion to try and find ways and means for improving Langford's safety standards. Chase had spotted several blatant violations that he had wasted no time in rectifying. Lax standards bred an attitude of carelessness, he asserted with a decisiveness that everyone had come to respect. The only problem was finding funds to implement a safety program. They had been discussing various possibilities when the door to Chase's office was flung wide open.

Startled, all three had turned to see the woman who was framed in the doorway.

Kate recognized her immediately as the woman who had been Chase's partner at the Mardi Gras ball in New Orleans. Platinum-blonde hair framed her face in gleaming waves against the stark black and white of her dress. It was obviously a designer model, simply cut, the lines of her sleek figure shown to their considerable advantage. Beautifully shaped legs extended beneath the pencil-slim skirt; black patent spike heels flattered her perfect ankles. The woman was a contrast of black and white from the top of her head to her feet.

Taking in the altogether-stunning picture she made, Kate's own blue linen skirt and pin-striped blouse, so right when she donned them that morning, suddenly seemed abysmally dull. She, who had never felt inadequate before another woman, wished she was anywhere but where she was.

"Chase, darling, I've missed you so." The woman sailed across the office and flung her arms around Chase's neck, kissing him with an intimacy that spoke for itself. She could not have been more proprietary if she had worn a sign stating "Chase Jamison is mine."

Ben and Kate shifted uncomfortably while Chase extricated himself from the blonde's clutches, his expression revealing only slight surprise overlaid with wry amusement.

"I didn't expect you, Gina," he drawled, drawing an immaculate handkerchief from his pocket and casually removing lipstick from his mouth.

As Kate and Ben waited, he finally remembered them and introduced the unexpected visitor as Gina Hart, "a friend."

"Gina and I go way back to about the first week I landed in Texas," he explained, his gaze familiar and friendly as he surveyed her attractions. The glint in his eye as he turned to Kate spurred her to deny the emotion that lanced her middle as she watched Gina Hart run a leisurely affectionate—and possessive—hand along the length of Chase's arm.

"Welcome to Mississippi, Miss Hart," she said in what she hoped was a reasonably civil tone.

Gina responded with the briefest touch of her cool fingers. As her eyes met Kate's dark blue gaze, they turned to a frigid shade of green. To Ben, she displayed all the charm that had apparently captivated Chase.

"I thought you were in Florida," Chase said, "with Blanche Masterson."

Gina turned predatory eyes toward Chase, smiling lazily, reminding Kate of a Siamese cat, the illusion magnified by the feline look in her eyes. "I'm on my way now," she explained, suppressed excitement in her eyes as she turned her face toward Chase.

"Blanche and Vince and a party of six others plan to depart from Miami in a few days. We're cruising for two weeks, Chase, and everybody wants you to come, too." She dragged her gaze from his, throwing a disparaging look around the office that relegated Kate and Ben to a level equal to the furniture. "You need some relief from all this."

Apparently, Chase was amused by her attitude, because he smiled as he observed the look on Kate's face. "Why don't I get back to you on this," he said to them hastily, cupping his hand familiarly under Gina's elbow and assisting her daintily into the chair close to the desk that had been Kate's father's. Gina subsided with sleek grace, a definite hint of triumph in the look she turned on Ben and Kate, mostly Kate.

"I do hope I haven't interrupted anything important," she said, crossing her perfect legs, the tone of her voice implying the utter absurdity of such a possibility.

Without replying, Kate turned on her heel and walked out. Later that day, she had spent a long time just staring blankly at her desk, marveling that neither Ben nor Naomi seemed to sense the chaotic state of her emotions. That searing shaft that penetrated her middle was jealousy, she admitted with wry self-knowledge. She had no claim on Chase, she argued to herself. He was a freewheeling bachelor, and his private life was none of her business. But the incident had shaken her, fueling an already growing dismay that Chase was becoming too important in her life.

That had been three days before, and since then, Kate had expected Chase to announce that he was leaving Baytown to join his friends on the cruise, but he gave no indication that he planned to leave Langford's destiny to her, or anyone else for that matter, even for two weeks.

Kate tossed her head impatiently, halting further speculation as to Chase's actions. She pulled up to the house and got out of the car, looking longingly at the beach. Sunlight glistened on the gently tossing waves of the Gulf. It would be nice to throw on a bikini and trudge across the sand, just lie idle for about an hour, but no . . .

With a regretful sigh, she bent over to lift half a dozen packages from the passenger seat of the car, gathering them into her arms. Balancing her handbag on top of the highest one, she managed to close the car door. Stepping gingerly, she reached the fence, pushing the squeaky gate open with her foot.

"Livvy!" she called, hoping her voice would carry into the sunroom, where her grandmother usually spent the afternoon. With relief, she heard the door open, and Olivia rushed to take some of the packages from her.

"Oh, you should have called sooner. I would have given you a hand," she chided, briskly depositing packages on the couch just inside the room. "I didn't hear you drive up, Kate."

Partially relieved of her burden, Kate's gaze was centered on the man lazily entrenched in the depths of the couch. At her entrance, he rose with easy male grace, a sardonic brow raised to meet the startled look that she was too late to suppress.

Chase! Quickly, she divested herself of her purchases and ran a shaky hand over the wind-tossed mane of her hair, conscious of her casual navy slacks and lime-green polo shirt. Was there any evidence of her earlier fantasies of Chase on her face? Her gaze faltered under the warmth of his look as she recalled her preoccupation.

"Can I help?" he drawled, obviously not affected by her sudden appearance. He reached a long arm to catch a parcel that was sliding to the floor.

Before he could touch it, she bent down, scooping it up. "Thanks, I can manage. Charlotte Scott and I grabbed some time this morning to do some neglected shopping, and I guess we got carried away." She looked at the mound of her purchases ruefully. "Charlotte must be a bad influence."

Breathless, she tried to recover from the unexpected sight of Chase. Her tongue seemed incapable of slowing down. Drat the man! What was it about him?

"Let me get you something to drink, Kate." Olivia disappeared into the kitchen, leaving Kate abandoned to her fate.

Chase gestured to the sofa, a roguish smile slanting his mouth. "Join us," he invited with all the assurance of a host while Kate fought an impulse to bristle indignantly. It was her house, she reminded herself firmly. Only the gleam in his brown eyes and her grandmother's sudden reappearance prevented her from calling that fact to his attention. She sank to the couch without a murmur and took the glass Olivia offered, concentrating on relaxing and recovering her composure. She sipped the iced drink, glad to have something to do other than gaze at Chase Jamison.

Nevertheless, she darted a covert glance at him from beneath lowered lashes, envying his air of complacence. He was certainly making himself at home, she thought testily, her gaze taking in the powerful width of his shoulders and the trim fit of faded jeans hugging muscular thighs as he sat down again, deliberately choosing the space next to her and arranging his long legs so that he was brushing against her just slightly. Her eyes traveled on down to his feet, which were thrust into thong leather sandals; before jerking her errant thoughts back into line, she noticed that even his feet were sexy. Her eyes returned to his face to find him watching her, totally at ease, a warmth in the gaze he ran over her.

Wishing he didn't disturb her, she turned resolutely to her grandmother. "What have you been up to?" she asked casually, conscious all the while of Chase's relentless gaze.

Olivia reseated herself, aiming an affectionate smile toward Chase, who returned the look with bland assurance, or so it looked to Kate's skeptical eye.

"Oh, just reminiscing about Joshua and Phillip," Livvy replied airily.

Kate's eyes narrowed sharply, instantly suspicious at the devilish glint he allowed her to see. She leaned over and set her drink carefully on the glass-topped table.

"Yes, well, things are certainly different now."

The glint was replaced by an openly mischievous smile. "Do I take the blame or the credit for that?" he drawled.

Kate's mouth compressed into a disgruntled line. "What's the difference?" she snapped.

If Chase's laugh was intended to further irritate her, it succeeded. "Well, if I take the blame, it's an insult, but if I take the credit, it's a compliment. Which is it, Kate?"

Taking a firm hold on her temper, Kate looked squarely into his eyes. Her lips parted to issue another cutting remark, but something stilled the impetuous reply. An innate sense of fair play prompted her to pause. Only a fool could remain unaware of the changes that Chase's management had brought about at Langford's in the past six weeks. He had a positive flair for ferreting out their problems and a keen intelligence for solving them, reluctant though she was to admit it.

Her lashes dropped, veiling the dark blue of her eyes. She smiled shortly. "The credit, of course, and you know it," she replied.

Her gaze lifted, meeting the inscrutable expression on his face. They exchanged a long, measured look, and Chase grinned suddenly, his eyes dancing with gold brown lights. "Well, I guess I'll never get a more generous compliment than that."

Her eyes searched suspiciously, suspecting sarcasm, but found no clue in his face.

He leaned over and placed his empty glass on the table and stood, powerful, lithe muscles rippling with the grace and form of an athlete, exuding the overwhelming male vitality that Kate's senses responded to in a familiar rush. No matter how she tried, she was powerless to control her physical response to Chase.

"Are you leaving?" She recognized the tiny stab of disappointment with a rueful sigh as he moved to the door. Her reactions to Chase kept her on tenterhooks when she was around him. She wished suddenly for the ease of their relationship years earlier when her self-confidence had been exceeded only by her conceit.

Deep in these unsettling thoughts, she became aware that Chase was studying her with every bit as much absorption as she studied him, and for a moment, she was robbed of all coherent thought. She bent over and lifted the empty glasses to busy her hands, her long, tawny hair falling around her face. Olivia rose, darting a quick glance between them, and then took the glasses from Kate and left the room. Alone together, silence stretched between them. It was a moment before Kate could find words, and when she did, they spoke simultaneously.

"Would you . . ."

"How is . . ."

They laughed, and Chase leaned against the frame of the door, the golden brown of his eyes roving her flushed features.

"Ladies first."

"I was just going to inquire about your quarters," she explained, breathless again. Surely that was a safe subject.

A smile still hovered at the corner of his mouth. Probably she amused him by her total lack of sophistication, Kate thought disparagingly, more disgusted with herself than ever. Would she always feel so vulnerable around Chase?

"I've done as much on it as I'm inclined to do, so I guess you could say I'm satisfied with it. In fact, that's what I was just going to say. If you want to judge firsthand, how about having dinner with me tonight?"

There was nothing she wanted more than to spend the evening alone with Chase, Kate acknowledged inwardly, and suddenly the thought of refusing was simply ridiculous. She looked into his eyes, acutely conscious of the attraction between them. She might try to deny it, but it was there, and it became more compelling with every encounter. Her eyes dropped to the dark brown hair curling crisply out of the vee of his shirt, and her fingers tingled with a desire to touch him.

"What time?" she heard herself ask, destroying any chance of pretending reluctance.

"I'll pick you up about seven," he said, straightening away from the door and stepping over the threshold. He turned, capturing her eyes with a look. "I'm going to the plant to check on a job. I don't expect to be there more than an hour at the most." His eyes dropped to her mouth, then swept quickly over her curving breasts and the lithe length of her legs. "Wear something to show off those gorgeous legs."

A bemused Kate was standing in the middle of the sunroom when Olivia entered a few minutes later. "Is Chase gone?" she inquired, a keen look assessing the softened line of Kate's mouth and the dark blue of her eyes.

"What?" At the sound of Olivia's voice, Kate turned. "Oh, yes, he's gone."

Her grandmother smiled. "I enjoyed his visit. He's an interesting man."

"What were you talking about?" Now that he was gone, Kate intended to get some specifics.

"Oh, this and that." Olivia looked pleased. "He's been very successful in his approach at the yard."

Reluctantly, Kate had to agree. She paused, her arms full of packages. "That's true; you would hardly recognize the place. There's such an air of . . . of industry at work now." A hint of regret darkened her eyes. "All it took was a little reorganization and someone to get out and search the market for more work," she murmured, deliberately understating Chase's expertise.

Her grandmother smiled wryly. "All it took was the right person at the right time, wouldn't you agree?"

Kate's expression hardened momentarily. "Chase certainly had the contacts, if that's what you mean. And, of course, he has only to speak, and everybody jumps!" Bitterness was etched in the set of her mouth.

Olivia frowned, watching Kate with concern. "Are you being quite fair in your assessment, Kate? I've never known you to show such antagonism, and it's affecting your judgment, I'm afraid. If you view Chase's actions as anything but a godsend to Langford's, then I think you should examine your own mind, dear. I don't want to seem critical, but who besides myself would dare to do a little plain speaking to you?" There was gentle remonstrance in Olivia's tone as she regarded her granddaughter, but a deeper concern could be seen in the searching intensity of her gaze. Kate could not fail to see that her grandmother was distressed, and she experienced a pang of sincere compunction.

"Have I been as bad as all that, Livvy?" Ruefully apologetic, Kate watched Olivia incline her head in wry acknowledgment.

She laughed shortly. If her own grandmother was going to defect to Chase's camp, then she was certainly fighting a losing battle. Nevertheless, a smile still hovered on her pretty mouth, her strong will reasserting itself without too much difficulty.

"Actually, you will be pleased to know that I'm properly impressed with Chase's methods," she said. "To give credit where credit is due, he is instigating plans for a repair yard, and in addition to the new construction he has managed to capture, we will begin to renovate used crafts. It will mean increased productivity and more employment. In fact, a ship which was behind schedule on the docks has been almost completed. Chase had to spend a lot of time personally trouble-shooting, but his time was well spent. Instead of losing money on the contract, Langford's will show a profit." She met Olivia's gaze with a glint of amusement in her eyes. "I guess the new blood is not all bad."

Olivia's eyes were bright with amusement. "Well, imagine that!"

Kate laughed again. "I must seem a fool to you, Livvy," she said ruefully. "I can't seem to make up my mind about Chase's motives." A tiny frown dented her forehead. "It was necessary to make some changes when he reorganized at the plant, and there were some very nervous people. But he did it so tactfully that practically no one was really hurt."

That much was true. The days had passed in a daze after that first illuminating morning. Chase's methods were distinctive, and Kate was much too astute a businesswoman not to recognize that fact. Acknowledging it now to her grandmother was surprisingly easy. It was only in her personal relationship with Chase that she was still as uncertain as she had been at seventeen.

"Yes, a small yard like Langford's won't hold much challenge for Chase now," Olivia said thoughtfully. "He'll be looking for another faltering business to turn around."

Kate threw a sharp glance at her grandmother. "Did he tell you he was leaving?"

Olivia turned blankly, seeing the startled look on Kate's face. "No, but it's only reasonable that he can't linger here indefinitely."

Gina Hart's visit proved that, but still, the thought of his leaving struck Kate like a blow. She picked up the last of the packages and turned away. Olivia was preoccupied with her own thoughts and missed the stricken look that darkened her eyes and compressed her mouth.

"Can I help you with those?" Olivia began to rise.

"No, no. It's not necessary, Livvy," Kate demurred, heading for the hallway. "I'm going to unpack these and put them away. I have a couple of hours before Chase arrives to pick me up. I think I'll take a long soak in the tub."

"Are you going out with Chase?" Olivia looked astonished.

"He's doing steaks on the grill," she replied with careful indifference. "It's no big deal."

But once in her room, she sank limply on the bed. Logically, Chase would leave just as soon as he had rejuvenated Langford Marine. He would place someone who was competent in a position of command, and the only connection he would retain would be a cursory glance at the monthly balance sheet that would cross his desk in Austin along with similar ones from the steadily rising number of businesses his corporation owned. It seemed so right to have him at Langford's. How had she allowed herself to forget what he really was? He was used to a more sophisticated social life, something that could never happen in Baytown, not to mention his relationship with Gina Hart, whatever it was. Kate tried to picture the sleek, sophisticated, totally urbane woman confined to Baytown and failed. Why hadn't she remembered that Chase's return to Baytown was certain to be a temporary thing? To him, Langford's was just another challenge in his entrepreneural endeavors. Fortunately, she was being brought face to face with reality, even though a little tardily. She must be more careful to resist the magnetic pull of attraction she felt for Chase. But she was steadily more drawn to him, and it wasn't going to be easy to see him go, she admitted with painful honesty.

Feeling sorry for herself was certainly not going to
help, she thought, rising and squaring her shoulders
purposefully. Work, thank goodness, had always
been a panacea, and Kate reached for her car keys,
seeking the escape that came easily when her mind
was occupied at Langford's. She would spend a
couple of hours at her desk, knowing from experience that nothing would intrude once she became
immersed in details.

She drove up to the shipyard facility only vaguely
aware of the nearly empty parking area. A handful
of cars indicated the presence of the Saturday crew
that Chase had mentioned, and she noted idly
Chase's own car drawn up in his usual space. He
would be down in the wet dock area where the crew
was performing some modifications to the soon-to-
be-delivered ship. The overtime crew was necessary
in order to meet the schedule for on-time delivery.

Kate stepped toward the main entrance of the
office complex, her head down, sorting through half
a dozen keys, when she became aware of a commo-
tion from the direction of the wet dock. She frowned
as she watched a couple of men heading toward the
ship; then, as they began to run, she realized something was wrong.

Quickly, she ran down the steps and headed
toward the chain-link fencing that enclosed the
manufacturing facility of Langford Marine. A cluster
of men could be seen on the deck of the ship. There
was an urgency about them as they hovered near
others, who were bent over the prone figure of a
man. Kate could see only long legs in faded jeans,
and her heart began an ominous, heavy thudding in
her chest, almost choking her with a wave of piercing
fear. She groped for her throat, her fingers suddenly
cold against her skin.

"Who is it?" she spoke urgently to a man whose

stained white overalls proclaimed him a painter. "What's happened?"

He glanced at her, then returned his gaze to the group huddled tensely on the deck. "You should have a hard hat on in this area, Miss Langford," he cautioned, his eyes not meeting hers again.

She was perfectly aware that she was in a hardhat zone, but her own safety was the last thing on her mind. "Who has been hurt?" she repeated in a voice that usually produced results.

"Looks like Chase," the painter said laconically. Then, as she sprang toward the dock and mounted the access platform, he yelled, "Hey, be careful up there!"

Kate was blind and deaf to everything but the sight of the two men who were leaning over Chase's ominously still form. She rushed forward, brushing past the silent group of men, who parted to let her through. Her knees shaking, she recognized Jim Nichols, who was positioning a folded garment of some sort under Chase's head. Nichols looked up, startled, as Kate sank on her haunches beside him, her eyes fastened on Chase's unconscious features.

"Is it bad?" She forced the words through bloodless lips, terrified by the sight of Chase's face, devoid of color, robbed of the vitality that set his features alive.

"I don't know. I don't think so," Nichols replied, his frown fading slightly as Chase moaned, flexing one knee weakly as though he would get up. Just as quickly, it sank back onto the deck, and he made another sound of pain.

"Don't try to move, Chase," she said, her hand reaching toward his face as though it had a will of its own. Her fingers carefully traced the line of his jaw, sliding upward to cup the side of his face tenderly. She could see the bruised lump at the edge of his temple, and her eyes widened fearfully as she noticed a trail of blood near his ear in the dark brown thatch of his hair.

She swallowed the lump that rose in her throat. Was he seriously injured? Her eyes closed on a swiftly murmured prayer. He couldn't be. Chase was too strong, too vital, for anything so preposterous. Dear God, was he dying? Her eyes sought the face of Jim Nichols, who had shifted slightly backward when Kate had dropped beside Chase.

"Someone get a doctor!" she cried, panic rising with the urgency of getting immediate medical attention to stave off something too horrible to be real.

"What the hell are you doing here?"

"Oh, God," Kate moaned, hearing the rasping words, noting with shocked relief the color returning to Chase's features. She watched while he lifted one hand and rubbed weakly across the rugged planes of his face, then groped for her, his fingers closing around the soft flesh of her arm. His gold-tipped lashes fluttered open, revealing pain-darkened eyes.

"It's not safe for you up here, honey. Go back down to the dock and wait for me there." Even returning from unconsciousness, Chase's instructions carried the unmistakable thread of command.

Her heart leaped at the casual endearment, but Kate didn't stop to dwell on it. She ignored him and sought Jim Nichols' eyes. "Did you call an ambulance?"

He hesitated, looking slightly discomfited. "Well, to tell the truth . . ."

She released an impatient breath. What was the matter with these men, she wondered wildly. Didn't they realize Chase might have a serious concussion? A man could die from a blow like the one he had just suffered so close to the temple. She shivered in dread.

"I don't need an ambulance," Chase stated flatly,

and ignoring her concerned protests, drew his knees up and rolled to his feet. He swayed slightly, and she thrust an arm around his waist, a fierce protectiveness entering her heart as he leaned against her.

Chase paused to direct a departing order. "Jim, get that equipment repaired before Monday morning. Dismiss today's crew before someone else gets hurt."

Nichols nodded, bending to pick up a white hard hat at his feet. "Reckon you'll be needin' a new hat," he observed, sinking two fingers into a deep dent in the protective helmet.

Kate's heart lurched sickeningly. Whatever had struck the hat would have done more than knock Chase unconscious, she saw with horror. Chase, glancing at her white face, moved purposefully, drawing her attention to the gangway slanting off the ship.

"I'm taking you to the hospital," she said grimly, picking her way at a slow pace around bins of equipment and cut steel. Although he was on his feet, Chase did not walk with his usual confidence. She felt his chest vibrate in a short laugh.

"Just a ride to my place will be sufficient, Florence."

"Florence?" Bewildered, she turned her face to his, encountering at close range warm amusement in the depths of his eyes.

"Nightingale."

"Oh."

They were at her car, and she reluctantly removed her arm from his waist, reaching clumsily to open the door, but Chase was before her. Watching while he folded himself into the car with masculine grace and no evidence of his recent trauma, Kate thought to herself that she might have been the one who had been knocked senseless. Apparently, it took more than a blow to the skull to unman Chase Jamison.

She sighed before moving around the car and seating herself behind the wheel.

"Chase, please let—"

He leaned against the headrest of the seat, and she noted the tense line of his mouth. "Don't argue, for once, Kate," he said. "I'll be okay with a couple of aspirins."

Frustrated, she pulled out of the parking lot and headed toward Fox Briar. Chase looked ill, but she knew him well enough to realize the futility of trying to persuade him to go to a doctor, so she drove silently past the big house on to Chase's cottage.

When she stopped the car, she got out and moved around to offer Chase whatever assistance he needed, but he was already out, moving with a peculiarly uneven gait toward the door.

"Chase . . ."

"It's not locked," he said, mounting the three steps and bracing himself against the iron handrail. He waited until she reached his side, eyes closed, swaying.

She looked into his face, and alarm washed over her again. Quickly, she thrust the door open and wrapped an arm around his waist, hoping he wouldn't fold before she reached a couch or something for him to lie down on.

She threw a quick look around, then stepped toward a contemporary pit which contained a multi-unit modular sofa. It was as broad as a bed, she noted, guiding Chase to it. He sank onto the cushioned surface with a relieved sound somewhere between a groan and a sigh.

"I'll be okay in a minute," he said, lying back and closing his eyes. His fingers slid down her arm and closed around her hand, so that she sank to the edge of the cushions, her worried eyes playing over his face, a chill fear present in the back of her mind as she realized he seemed to be instantly asleep.

Hastily, she rose, detaching her hand from his slack fingers, and glanced around for the telephone. It was mounted on the wall in the tiny kitchen, and she ran over to it. Whether he wanted one or not, she intended to call a doctor. A concussion was nothing to fool around with.

Chapter Eight

Chase did not stir until the doctor arrived. Fortunately, Michael Browne was a neighbor and a friend of Kate's. After one look at her, he spent the first few moments soothing her with a few professional-sounding phrases before bending over his patient. At the first touch of the physician's fingers to the wound, Chase winced and opened his eyes.

"I don't think it's serious," Chase said, his eyes seeking Kate's anxious ones. Was he searching for her? Did he want her with him?

Michael smiled, pulling an instrument out of his bag and efficiently directing its lighted tip into Chase's right eye. "I believe that's my line," he observed mildly, examining the left one with equal skill. "But I'll bet you have the granddaddy of all headaches right this minute, don't you?"

Chase's mouth quirked wryly. "In a word, yes."

"Actually, I don't think you have a concussion," Michael ventured after cleaning the wound, "but you shouldn't take any foolish chances with a blow to the head like this. Don't stay alone tonight, and if you have any nausea, call me right away."

He smiled reassuringly at Kate. "Fix him something light for dinner, Kate, and give him two of these every three or four hours for the headache." He handed her a small bottle, then stood briskly, moving toward the door. "That's about all you can do besides rest in bed." With a bright, amused glance at her flushed face, Michael Browne left.

Silence stretched between them as she stared into his eyes.

"Satisfied?" he mocked.

Her eyes faltered before his, and she turned toward the kitchen. "I'm going to get you a glass of water, and you can take two pills now. If you will just lie still after you take them, the pain will probably ease off."

"Okay."

She turned startled eyes on him, the glass suspended under the water faucet. "You mean you're going to listen to me for once?" She came toward him carrying the water and medicine.

"I mean that I have a devil of a headache, and I'm at a disadvantage because of it. Exhilarating as our bouts are, I'm afraid I'm not up to one of them at the moment." He groaned, rolling his body into an upright position, waiting for her to shake two tablets from the bottle. "Now if you'll lower that glass a couple of feet so I can reach it—"

"Oh, I'm sorry!" She gave him the glass, watching while he swallowed the pills, one part of her mind intrigued by his remarks.

"What happened, Chase?" She was only now realizing that she didn't know how the accident happened. She knew only the aftermath of a clenching fear that had seized her when she had realized Chase was hurt.

Chase eased back against the cushions, pulling a loose one from a bunch of throw pillows that were scattered over the pit. "As you know, the equipment in the yard isn't up to standards safetywise. A cable snapped which was holding steel suspended from a crane, and I happened to be in the wrong place at the right time."

"Thank God you wore a hard hat." Kate bit her bottom lip to control its tremor, then swallowed thickly. "You could have been killed."

Chase turned his head on the pillow, his gaze locking with hers. "Yeah, and I had big plans for tonight."

"Chase!" Her voice came in a strangled tone. "Don't talk like that. This could have been a serious accident. We don't even know for sure that you are all right. You heard what Michael said. You could still take a turn for the worse."

"Are you volunteering to keep watch throughout the wee hours?" One brow was arched suggestively.

"You can't stay alone. Michael said—"

"I heard what he said," Chase returned quietly. "But I think Michael assumed there was something more intimate in our relationship than the guarded, almost professional association we've managed to maintain . . . so far, that is."

Kate wandered over to the sliding-glass doors, her gaze fastened blindly on the churning waters of the Gulf, a scant hundred yards from the cottage. Her stomach felt just as unsettled as the white-capped surface. "I know what he thought," she murmured, recalling Michael's shrewdly amused looks, "but I don't intend to leave you alone after what he said, no matter what anyone thinks."

"You don't have to bother, Kate," Chase said tiredly, his voice slurring as the effects of the tablets increased. "I have a housekeeper who will be in tomorrow morning. She already prepared the trimmings for dinner tonight. All we need to do is put the steaks on the grill. I promised you dinner, and dinner you will get."

Kate turned away from the window and stared incredulously, her eyes noting the aggressive line of his jaw even though his eyes were closed. "You aren't having steak tonight," she stated firmly. "You heard what Michael—"

"Spare me any more of Michael's worthy quotes. I'll be fine in a few minutes. You can set the table," he suggested, yawning widely. "By the time you . . ."

But the strong narcotics had a telling effect, and he was once again asleep.

Kate eased down on the edge of the cushion, her gaze lingering on Chase's features, relaxed in sleep. The firm line of his mouth was slightly vulnerable; otherwise, his face still wore the unmistakable stamp of strength and rugged masculinity. Her fingers reached out tentatively, touching the clean line of his cheek, and he murmured something, turning his mouth into her palm. Kate was astonished by the rush of tenderness that swept over her. What was it about this man that so easily captivated her? True, he had narrowly escaped a serious injury, but she told herself she would be relieved and happy to see anyone spared from such a fate. But deep within her, she recognized a stronger, more compelling force at work.

The direction of her thoughts was disturbing, and Kate shifted gently away from the warm length of Chase's body, withdrawing her hand and rising to move toward the telephone.

She called Livvy and explained the circumstances, reporting Michael Browne's diagnosis as well as his statement that Chase not be left alone. Livvy exclaimed her concern. If she thought Kate's firm resolve to stay overnight was strange, then she was too tactful to say so. Kate rang off, and immediately her gaze swung back to Chase, sprawled on the sofa.

Unable to remain very far from him, she stepped down into the pit onto a smoky-blue carpet. Lights were concealed beneath the exposed beams of the cathedral ceiling, but she decided not to turn them on in case they bothered Chase. She moved closer, her eyes dark with concern, noting the easy rise and fall of his chest with some lessening of the tight band of worry that was lodged deep inside her. She looked around the cottage, vaguely aware of the blend of pale beige and blue and brown, colors suiting Chase's status as a lone male, self-reliant and self-sufficient.

Somehow that thought was depressing, and she shivered in the cooling atmosphere. Chase was going to need a blanket, and she started toward the short hallway to one of the two bedrooms to search for one. The first room was obviously Chase's. A dark chocolate and blue Indian-motif spread covered the bed. The interior of the closet revealed extra blankets. She removed two and returned to the great-room where she carefully covered him, debating whether or not to remove his shoes, finally deciding against disturbing him in any way. If he awakened, the pain would no doubt return.

A search of the kitchen and refrigerator did indeed reveal that everything was in readiness for their dinner, but if Chase woke up hungry, Kate assured herself there were eggs for a light omelet and even a can of New England clam chowder if he insisted on more. Her own appetite had vanished with the first glimpse of Chase unconscious. She made herself a cup of tea, careful to avoid making any noise, and settled herself down in a corner of the pit to wait.

Two hours later, Chase stirred, his eyes focusing

on her in blank confusion at first, then closing wryly as memory returned.

"What time is it?" he asked, his palm raking across his face before falling to his side.

Kate's eyes flicked to her watch. "Only nine o'clock. How's the headache?"

"Better. I'm hungry. Did you fix the steaks?" He shoved the blanket aside and sat up, moving gingerly, Kate noted. She watched him dubiously. He had been quick to deny a headache, but when he stood and began to stride purposefully toward the kitchen, she supposed the pain really had departed. She unfolded her legs and stood up.

"I didn't fix the steaks, Chase. You heard what Michael said."

He opened his mouth to argue, but she forestalled him. "Since it's a little late to be eating something heavy as a steak, why don't I make us both an omelet," she suggested. "If you want something else, there's clam chowder to go with it."

He looked unconvinced. "It's hardly what I promised you." His eyes swept her figure, and she was uncomfortably aware of her crumpled blouse and lack of makeup. Her linen slacks had lost their sharp creases.

"In that get-up, I don't even get a glimpse of your legs," he grumbled, a gleam in his eyes. "And that was a specific condition you'll recall when I asked you to dinner."

Unaccustomed to a teasing Chase, Kate blushed. "You're right. If I don't get a steak, all conditions are null and void," she returned playfully, watching him from beneath her lashes.

They exchanged a long look. Kate was breathless, and her pulse raced as Chase's eyes blazed over her features. He took a step forward but was halted by a firm rap on the door.

"Hold that thought," he murmured, reluctantly dragging his gaze from her parted lips, scowling when the insistent knocking continued.

A man Kate recognized as one of the group who had assisted Chase when he had been hurt on the deck of the ship stood awkwardly extending some keys, which he dropped into Chase's outstretched hand.

"Jim told me to drive your car over here, Mr. Jamison. Looks like there's a squall brewing," he observed, indicating the rough surface of the Gulf with a quick gesture of his head. "Could get some damage if it's not under your carport."

"Thanks, Ray." Chase accepted the keys, then braced one arm against the door frame, his weight on one leg. "Is Jim battening down and securing everything at the yard?"

The man nodded. "Yes, sir. He said you shouldn't worry." Then, hesitantly, but with genuine concern, he asked, "You feeling okay, Mr. Jamison?"

Chase flexed broad shoulders and shifted away from the door. "I'm fine, Ray. Get on back and give Jim a hand." He watched while Ray leaned against gusting wind and then climbed into a waiting car. He closed the door and turned, tossing the car keys onto the low glass table.

The feeling of intimacy intensified when his eyes sought hers. Kate's pulse reacted wildly, while an inner voice urged caution. Although there was very little light in the room, it appeared through the triple panel of glass doors, that the weather was deteriorating rapidly. Illuminated by the occasional flashes of lightning, Kate could see the sandy beach and the surf rushing in to slam against the shore.

"I'll fix you a drink," Chase said suddenly, and walked to the kitchen.

"Oh, you don't have to bother," she began hesitantly. "I hope you don't intend to drink while taking those narcotics." Worriedly, she watched while he filled a wineglass.

"Not to worry, Florence," he said, his eyes wry. "I plan to have plain water."

She relaxed a little, settling into the sofa and balancing her drink carefully when Chase sat down beside her. He watched her, his eyes holding hers over the rim of her glass. It would be so easy to drown in the richness of his gaze, but Kate wrenched her eyes from the compelling warmth and sought frantically for her faltering composure.

Primly, she sipped her drink like an adolescent on her first date, searching her suddenly empty mind for a topic to relieve the tension that gripped her.

"This is hindsight," she began, "but I'm thinking that today's accident was practically inevitable considering the age of some of our equipment." Some of the strain eased as she forced her mind into more familiar territory. "You've made a lot of improvements, but there are still many things that require refurbishing."

Chase was silent for a moment. "Do I get the idea that you don't resent me quite so much as when I first appeared in Baytown?"

Kate eyed the amber surface of her drink and frowned. Her effort to channel conversation to impersonal topics had been ignored by Chase. "I can see why you might think that," she said carefully, thankful he didn't know all the reasons for her reactions to him.

He laughed shortly. "I can see I'm not entirely free from suspicion even now." His mouth thinned with the words, but Kate refused to acknowledge that his expression contained a hint of hurt.

"I can't believe my opinion matters one way or another," she retorted.

He made a skeptical sound in his throat. "Why do I get the feeling you see me as an intruder?" She felt the tension in him, and her eyes were drawn to his.

"It would be extremely foolish and ungrateful of me to admit something like that," she replied stiffly. "After all, you've single-handedly solved all our problems."

He stared at her as if suspecting sarcasm.

"I would hardly say I've solved all the problems," he countered shortly.

"Maybe not all of them, but the tide has turned, and the employees know it. The possibility of a secure future has done wonders for the morale at the plant."

"We won't make a profit for a couple of years," Chase cautioned as though her cataloguing his accomplishments was not exactly pleasing to him. "We'll probably lose money the first year and possibly the second."

"Yes, of course," Kate replied impatiently. "I know enough about business to realize that, but I'm certain your corporation must have calculated the risks when they acquired Langford. Didn't you decide future growth would compensate for that initial loss?"

"Well, it's more of a long shot than you seem to think at this point," he insisted with almost stubborn candor. "What gains we make this year will have to go back into capital outlay for the new equipment. Jim Nichols manages remarkably well right now, but he's falling behind every day. It's an absolute necessity that his shop be refurbished."

"I know," she agreed, the businesswoman in her responding enthusiastically. "I told Ron weeks ago that Jim had to have that equipment, but he—"

"I'm certain you got no sympathy from Ron."

Her first impulse was to rush to Ron's defense, but again her innate honesty compelled her to pause. "I know what you think, Chase," she began, determined to explain Ron's apparent lack of interest without sounding disloyal to her brother.

"You don't know what I think," he interrupted bluntly, "but I'll tell you. I have some connections around the country who are doing some experimental design work in engines. I've already mentioned it to Ron, and he's meeting with them this weekend in New Orleans. I've no doubt he'll be resigning Monday morning." Amusement glinted as he watched her reaction. "He would probably resign tomorrow if it wasn't Sunday."

Kate was speechless, torn between indignation and pleased surprise. If it meant that Ron could develop his precious engines, he would not hesitate to leave home at once, and Chase knew that as well as she. He had only stayed in the family business out of a sense of duty, and now, because of Chase, he was free. But she was hurt because he had accepted Chase's assistance without a word to her.

"You're not his mother, Kate," Chase said quietly, his intent gaze correctly interpreting her hurt silence. "Give him a chance to do what he does best. Just because you thrive on competition and cost analysis sheets doesn't mean your brother shares your fascination for the business world."

Was that the way Chase saw her? It sounded dull and stodgy when put into words, but why should she care about his opinion of her? If he didn't think of her as particularly attractive—because his description of her had a ring of contempt, hadn't it?—then she didn't care. She no longer yearned for approval from Chase. Did she?

She smiled tightly. "It looks like my family is going to be forever in your debt," she said, almost choking on the words. "First, you generously allow us to remain at Fox Briar, and then you salvage the family business at considerable personal risk, as it turned out today. Now you've delivered Ron from his responsibilities by arranging a perfectly respectable opportunity for him to escape. How can we ever repay you?"

"I don't want your gratitude, for God's sake!" he exploded, rising to his feet, his face tautly set.

Startled and puzzled by his reaction, she blinked up into his furious gaze. "I . . . I didn't . . ." She was suddenly afraid she might have shattered the tenuous harmony that they had managed to achieve, however brief. But beneath it all, she had been subtly aware of a turbulence in Chase's manner since he woke up. What was bothering him?

"Let's have something to eat." Interrupting her disjointed thoughts, he pivoted sharply, his fingers going briefly to his head. He was probably in pain, but Kate saw by the look on his face he would not welcome any solicitousness on her part. Just then, through the wide view framed by the glass doors, a bright streak of lightning flared, its blue white flash reflecting off the choppy whitecaps of the Gulf.

"Heat lightning," Chase murmured, his brooding gaze straying outward.

"I hope it's not too severe," Kate remarked, feeling the natural phenomena increasing the tension crackling the atmosphere between them. "Now that I think about it, storm clouds have been threatening all afternoon."

"I noticed." Chase issued the words dryly, and something in his voice caused Kate's pulse to speed up.

"Why don't I make that omelet?" She moved quickly before he could deliver another of his double-edged remarks.

Swiftly and with feminine instinct for the tiny kitchen's layout, Kate prepared omelets and chowder, which they ate with very little conversation. She watched Chase with a surreptitious eye, noting a returning tautness in his face as he rose from the table, walking gingerly. Finally, she couldn't bear to keep quiet.

"Chase, why don't you go to bed? Take some more of those tablets and—"

"Won't Olivia wonder where you are?" He stepped down into the pit, taking care to ease himself onto the sofa.

"I've already called her and explained what happened." She glanced toward the glass doors where rising wind caught and hurled leaves and debris against the cottage. She rose purposefully. "I'm going to move my car under the carport alongside yours. It looks as though the wind is really whipping up." The first drops of rain spattered against the glass.

"Stay inside," Chase ordered, but before he could prevent it, she had grabbed her keys and slipped through the front door. Strong winds whipped against her legs, tossing her hair into a hopeless tangle, but the car was certain to be damaged if she didn't get it under some sort of shelter.

Even so, she returned to the cottage breathless and disheveled and soaked from the rain, which had begun in earnest.

Chase lay on the cushions, watching her with an unfathomable look in his eye. She laughed, suddenly discovering there was nowhere else in the world she would rather be at this moment.

"What's so funny?" he asked, an indulgent gleam appearing, tilting his mouth.

Her eyes ran over him hungrily, but she turned, unwilling for him to read what was certain to be written for the world to see on her face. She busied her hands collecting the dishes from the table, and placing them in the dishwasher, she turned off the

...t in the kitchen. Immediately, the cottage took on the intimate, dimly lit atmosphere that had pervaded it before supper.

"Come here." Chase leaned against the pillows, watching lazily with obvious pleasure while she moved warily toward him. Catching her hand, he tugged gently until she sank down beside him.

"You're wet," he observed, running an exploratory hand over her shirt, lingering warmly against her midriff. "Go in my bedroom closet and get my robe. I don't ever use it, so you'll have to search for it, but I think it's hanging to the left of my shirts."

Issuing instructions as casually as if he were requesting a copy of that day's newspaper, Chase waited expectantly for her to respond. She began a halting refusal.

"That's okay. I can just . . . I'm perfectly all right, Chase. I don't need . . ."

Sighing wearily, he started to pull himself up.

"Wait!" She placed a hand on his shoulder, and he eased backward.

Why did it matter, anyway? she asked herself as she rummaged through his closet. Her blouse and pants were sticking clammily to her skin, and the soft navy velour of Chase's robe would be much more comfortable. Besides, he could hardly pose much of a threat to her with a severe headache.

Swiftly, she stepped out of her clothes, but she stubbornly refused to remove her minuscule lace panties. She did not stop to analyze that tiny precaution.

When she reappeared, his smile winged across the room, assaulting her defenses with the force of the gale winds whistling outside. "That thing looks a lot better on you than it does on me." His eyes traveled over her, pausing at the expanse of legs revealed in the thigh-length garment. "Hmmm, honoring our bargain, I see." He reached out a hand, and she settled against him as naturally as if she spent every night of her life in Chase's arms.

"I feel ridiculous in this thing," she said shakily, close proximity stealing her breath. "Besides being too short, it's ten times too big."

"One size fits all," he said against her neck, his mouth warm as he nuzzled one ear lobe.

"It doesn't fit me," she argued weakly, her bones turning to liquid beneath the heated seduction he was conducting.

"Don't worry," he husked in her ear. "You look beautiful no matter what you have on." He shifted slightly, his hands pulling her more fully against him, and winced with the movement.

"Be still," Kate whispered, her heart thudding so hard that it was incredible that he wasn't aware of it. "You'll bring back your headache."

"That's not what's aching," he murmured, drawing her body up against the full, warm length of his. "Fix the blanket," he managed to say, although without his usual authority, and she could tell from the deepening tones of his voice that he was allowing himself to relax totally.

Some remaining vestige of sanity issued a faint protest, but there was no contest. Kate told herself she would humor him for only a few minutes. The painkillers would plunge him into a deep sleep, and he wouldn't even know when she got up and found a more respectable location to spend the remainder of the night. But for the moment, she savored the delight of lying in Chase's arms, even fancying for a minute that for once he needed her. Carefully, she pulled the edges of the blanket over them both, and with Chase's deep, even breathing in her ear blending with the outside sounds of lashing wind and rain and rumbling thunder, she slept.

Chapter Nine

An unaccustomed warmth lay heavy across her legs. Kate struggled up from the depths of a sleep that had been interspersed with fuzzy and insubstantial dreams. She could not recall them, but she knew they had been full of pleasure, sweetly satisfying. Another sensation, also unaccustomed, was centered on her midriff, a lazy stroking warmth. It produced a delicious response, and she turned into it, her own hands reaching, instinctively reacting to the awakening of her body even before her mind identified this delightful morning magic.

Chase's heavily muscled frame was turned to her, his hands moving inside the now-loosened robe, unhurriedly, languidly, stroking her sensitized skin. Maybe it was the effect of her dreams, or maybe it was a reaction to Chase's near-tragic accident or a combination of both, but whatever it was, it was a heady sensation, and right now she was incapable of resisting it. She didn't open her eyes, unwilling to assess whatever message she might read in his expression. She lifted her face at the urging of his hands buried in her hair, and her lips parted, eagerly welcoming Chase's gentle demand.

His mouth claimed hers in a kiss that was at once hungrily possessive, searchingly satisfying. With probing mastery, he swept her away on the crest of a wave of desire comparable to any turbulence outside. Kate could not get close enough to him, and with a rough sound, his arms tightened around her, the palm of one hand curling around her rib cage, his thumb resting under the vulnerable swell of her breast. Insatiably, he invaded the silken warmth of her mouth with urgent, drugging kisses, awakening in her a frenzied need that could only be fulfilled with this man.

Suddenly, he abandoned her mouth, his lips feathering along her cheek, beneath her jaw, grazing the side of her throat while progressing inexorably toward the deep, scented valley of her breasts. Outside, the distant rumble of thunder echoed the wild beating of her heart, urging a response to him that she knew would seal her fate as his forever.

Kate's veins sang with delight as she sensed Chase's unbridled arousal. His hand trembled as he cupped one swelling, aching breast. Mindlessly, her hands groped for his head, her fingers delving gently into the thick, brown richness of his hair, guiding him urgently. Her senses escalating wildly, she was aware only of a deep, compelling need for all of him. When his mouth closed warmly on the throbbing tip, delight coursed through her, drawing a deep sigh of satisfaction. She gasped when his tongue curled moistly around the tight bud, moaning softly at the strange, gentle abrasion surely and expertly flexed against her tingling flesh, almost whimpering with delight when he moved to her other breast, patiently and lovingly drawing out the pleasure that he wrought.

With both palms against the muscled cords of his neck, she guided his mouth to hers, kissing him with an abandon that could no longer shock her. For how could making love with the only man she had ever loved be shocking? Discovery and joy were intermingled as she sought to convey without words the pleasure and rapture his touch could bring to her and wanting, needing, to pleasure him in return.

Chase's breathing was ragged and uneven as he sensed her deep response. Sometime in the night, he had shed his shirt, she discovered, her questing hands sliding over smoothly muscled flesh. He aided her unskilled hands, guiding her fingers through the erotically abrasive mat of hair on his chest, wordlessly encouraging when her palms roamed the hard plane of his flat stomach, inhaling sharply when she grasped the muscled skin of his shoulders and arched her body into his accommodating male contours.

She breathed his name huskily against his ear, her lips pressing eager little kisses against his neck, into his hair, inhaling the scent of him and glorying in it.

The robe was discarded. Only her tiny lace panties remained between Chase's heated flesh and her own equally abandoned inhibitions. Kate's mind went blank, and she yielded to the demand of clamoring desire.

For a moment, neither she nor Chase was capable of any coherent response to the loud noice that shattered the intimate mood induced by their deep languor.

Chase groaned, a frustrated, anguished sound. "Wait . . ." he protested in a hoarse voice to the incessant banging at the door. Burying his face in her hair, his hands moved restlessly against the silken skin of her thighs, up over the swell of her hips. The noise persisted. Suddenly, his muscles relaxed against her, and he grasped her head between his hands, pressing a hard, urgent kiss to her lips.

"I don't know who that is, but it had better be a matter of life and death," he grated, rolling off her and moving grimly to the door.

Kate watched him, her eyes dark with lingering passion. She sat up, slipping her arms back into the blue robe and belting it securely.

"Yeah, what is it?" Chase stood, head bent, chest heaving as though he had run a mile. One hand was pressed flat against the door. Kate's eyes drank in the sight of him, tanned and hard, the flesh of his stomach tight and shaded with dark hair. He still wore his jeans. Had she removed his shirt? she wondered blankly. She didn't remember, and as blood suffused her face, she realized she didn't care.

"Jim Nichols, Chase. There's trouble at the yard."

"Just a minute, Jim."

Quickly, Chase strode over to the pit and leaned across Kate, retrieving his shirt and thrusting his arms into it. His eyes locked with hers. He bent and swiftly kissed her mouth. "Don't go away, darling. Nothing short of a calamity could make me leave you right now." He straightened up, his eyes still on her face. "Beautiful," he murmured, dragging his gaze from her mouth and drawing a long, ragged breath. He walked to the door, opened it and slipped outside.

Kate could hear the sound of Jim Nichols' deep voice as he spoke to Chase. She recognized an urgency in his tone and instinctively suspected the high winds probably caused some damage at the plant. She made her way to Chase's bedroom to retrieve her pants and shirt, grimacing when they were still damp. She would just have to wear the robe home. Glancing at the clock, she saw it was just after seven in the morning. Through windows studded with raindrops, she noted the storm seemed to have spent itself, but it was still drizzling rain.

"Well, it *was* a calamity," Chase said with a rueful twist of his mouth, his fingers securing the buttons on his shirt. "The winds blew a crane into the side of a partially constructed section of one of our new ships. There's more damage to some of the outbuildings, too. Jim's on his way back to the plant, and I promised to meet him as soon as I can." He rolled up the sleeves of his shirt and stuffed the tail into his jeans.

Her eyes moved over his face anxiously. "Should you do that, Chase? How about your head?"

He shrugged aside her concern. "It's fine now." He grinned, coming up to her and sliding one hand around her neck beneath her hair. "A result of excellent nursing care, I reckon."

Her lashes fell, shielding the ready response she knew would be in her eyes. "Well, I'm going to go home if you don't need me anymore."

The teasing light faded from his eyes. "Don't ever say that."

"What?" Her tongue flicked out to moisten dry lips.

He bent to capture it, his mouth gentle on hers. "That I don't need you."

"Oh, Chase, you don't have to—"

He interrupted her with another kiss. "I know what I have to do, but now is not the time." He caught her arm, propelling her toward the door and closing it behind them. "Right now I have to get you home, and then I have to bail out Langford Marine."

"Yuck," she yelped. "What an awful pun! And you don't need to drive me home. I've got my own car, remember?"

He ignored her, guiding her around to the passenger side of his car. "Get in. I'll have someone drive your car home within the hour." He slammed the door on any further argument.

The brief drive from the cottage to the main house was accomplished in silence, each of them occupied with their own thoughts, Kate supposed. When Chase drew up to the door at Fox Briar, he turned to her, resting one arm on the back of the car seat.

"I don't want to leave you," he said huskily, his fingers tangling in the hair at her nape, eyes roaming her face, lingering hungrily on her well-kissed mouth.

Under the onslaught of his gaze, Kate's heart thudded in her chest, and heat coursed through her veins all the way to the tips of her toes. She was helpless under the spell of her response to Chase.

"Thanks for the ride," she whispered, her lashes fluttering against her cheeks in an attempt to conceal her vulnerability to the blatant message in his eyes. "I hope you will be careful and avoid anything strenuous," she began earnestly. "The men can do the heavy work. You can just kind of oversee."

"Be quiet," he commanded, leaning toward her, his hand curling behind her neck, pulling her forward to meet his descending mouth. "You talk too much."

She sighed, subsiding weakly under the warm possession of his kiss, her arms somehow finding their way around his neck, enfolding him and claiming him with an answering hunger.

She lost track of time, aware only of the spiraling pleasure Chase evoked. But after a blissful few minutes, he released her, and reaching for each of her hands, reluctantly removed them from around his neck. He bent his head, kissing her palms, grazing the sensitive area with his tongue. He tucked them in a prim fold in her lap and got out of the car, ignoring the wet drizzle to stride around to her side and pull her door open. She began a stunned protest as she realized his intent, but he hauled her out into the rain and swung her into his arms.

She squealed in startled reaction, her arms automatically encircling his neck when he ignored her pleas to put her down. The distance to the front steps and the huge door was covered in long strides. He didn't hesitate until they were inside.

"Chase, you shouldn't—"

"I couldn't resist." With one foot, he kicked the door closed. His eyes skimmed over her flushed face, barely an inch away from his own, then traveled lazily down to the hollow of her throat, coming to rest on the expanse of creamy skin bared by the provocative gap of the oversized lapels of his robe. Kate felt the sensual response of Chase's body.

A hard, searing kiss destroyed her ability to think as his warm mouth covered hers in a devouring, drugging sweetness and drew an instantaneous response. Her arms tightened around the column of his neck, while a languorous warmth turned her bones to water, pervading her senses with a wine-dark rapture as his tongue intertwined with her own in a mutual commingling, warm with desire.

She knew she should resist him, but she simply could not rally any defense against him. The driving possession of his kiss rendered her helpless to do anything except yield with the same mindlessness that swamped her every time Chase touched her. But it wasn't just the sensual expertise that Chase employed that captivated Kate every time. It was the absolute rightness of being in his arms. It was so natural that everything in Kate rejoiced at the sense of coming home that being with Chase brought. That was why she couldn't manufacture any resistance. Did he feel an answering response, or was it all just another casual sexual encounter to Chase?"

"Am I interrupting anything?" A hard voice jarred the intimacy of the moment.

In Kate's aroused state, she failed to react for a few seconds, but other than an almost imperceptible tensing of his body, Chase ignored the untimely interruption.

With a lazy indifference, taking his time, he released her mouth, easing her downward so that she stood in the brief toweling robe against him. She had to use the rock-hard steadiness of his frame as a support; otherwise, her trembling legs would have folded beneath her.

"Devereaux." Chase acknowledged Mark's appearance with a sardonic tilt of his head, but his eyes had a hard glint when he faced the younger man.

"What are you doing here, Mark?" Kate asked, wondering in confusion if she had failed to recall making a date. Under his accusing regard, she felt betraying color stain her cheeks, but after what he had witnessed, there seemed little she could say. She was powerless to deny her passionate response to Chase even if she'd been inclined to do so.

"I had some business on the coast, and I got caught in the sudden tropical storm on my way home," he explained, subjecting her to a hard look as she leaned against Chase. "Olivia thoughtfully invited me to stay overnight. I'm glad now that I did."

Kate bit back the involuntary reaction that Mark's insinuation prompted. The last thing she wanted was to answer the questions she read in the proprietary way he was regarding her in the borrowed robe. She had never given Mark reason to believe he had any claim on her. To make matters worse, she sensed a hostile tension in the taut muscles of Chase's body pressed against her. Male territorial instinct, she thought cynically, doubting any depth of feeling for her on Chase's part but knowing him well enough to believe he wouldn't want to share any woman who interested him even temporarily.

"As you can see," Chase began shortly, "Kate is tired from a very long night. She is also wet and needs to change. . . ." He turned a possessive gaze onto her, male appreciation in his sherry-brown eyes.

Mark's hostile gaze centered on Chase. "What happened to her clothes?"

"Just a minute, Mark," Kate began indignantly.

"I must have forgotten to return them," Chase said wickedly.

At once, they turned shocked eyes toward him. "Look here," Mark began, ignoring the challenge inherent in Chase's words, "just what is going on?" He turned angry eyes to Kate. "I believe you owe me an explanation, Kate."

"I don't believe she does," Chase refuted flatly, a grim coldness in his eyes. "Kate doesn't answer to any man . . . yet."

"Do you mind?" She directed a furious look between both men, indignation replacing the earlier embarrassed color in her cheeks. "Both of you are sounding very possessive, and I've given neither of you the right to . . . to scrabble over me like some kind of . . . of object!" She turned flashing eyes to Mark, who blinked uncertainly, wary of her temper from past experience. "You go too far, Mark, when you presume to question my behavior or my attire. There's a perfectly reasonable explanation for my appearance, but it will be a cold day in you-know-where before you hear it."

She whirled furiously at the smothered sound coming from Chase. "I'm also getting some pretty strong vibrations from you, Mr. Jamison, and you know where you can take them."

Chase swung his gaze to hers for a moment, his

look indecipherable, a little impatient when she tried to move out of his arms. Mark jerked forward, thrusting a hand to Kate, then halting abruptly at the fierce blaze in Chase's eyes.

Kate's agitated breathing was the only sound for a moment as the two men stood squared off, the tension throbbing between them for unmeasured seconds.

Chase detached his hard gaze from Mark's more defiant one and sought Kate's eyes. His look contained an unmistakable hint of possession, but his features were arranged in a rigid expression. Kate felt an almost irresistible urge to laugh out loud as she considered how very rarely Chase must find himself with little recourse except to retreat. Because short of making some kind of public statement that his intentions were honorable, he could say nothing without compromising her already suspect reputation. She knew Chase would never allow himself to be manipulated into something that might jeopardize his carefree bachelor life style.

"You had your chance, Devereaux," Chase said, a hard inflection in his voice. "Now, contrary to what Kate says, I'm taking a very possessive attitude toward her."

Wrenching herself from the steel band of his hold, Kate stared incredulously into Chase's eyes. She searched the suddenly closed features for a hint of mischief or any emotion that would account for his incredible statement but could read nothing in his steady regard.

"Is this true?" Mark demanded of Kate, and it was with an effort that she dragged her stunned gaze away from the inscrutable message in Chase's look.

"Is what true?" she managed, distracted and not a little bewildered. What was Chase up to?

"Is it true that you don't owe me an explanation because you have something going with this—" His mouth twisted in a sneer. "You have really played me for a fool."

"If the shoe fits," Chase quoted in a dry voice.

"Will you shut up!" Kate cried, convinced she was in a crazy dream and any moment would wake up. It wouldn't surprise her if the Mad Hatter entered next.

Mark hesitated, struggling to retain some of his dignity, and then shouldered past them to yank the door open and dash out into the rain without another backward look.

Kate turned toward Chase, anger and indignation causing her to tremble. "How dare you," she whispered in a white-hot rage. "How dare you!"

There was a complacent look about his mouth. "Why are you so angry? How many men do you need dancing attendance, Kate? Isn't that your philosophy . . . keep them dangling by playing them all against each other?"

"Get out," she said shakily. "You don't know anything about me, so get out."

He watched her draw the belt of the robe more securely around her waist, his eyes sweeping a comprehensive survey over her long, shapely legs and upward to the curve of her hips, dwelling on the agitated rise and fall of her breasts. "I know Mark Devereaux is not for you, Kate. I've merely disposed of him quickly and as painlessly as possible."

Rigid with rage, Kate drew herself up to her full height and turned on her heel. She couldn't get rid of him by demanding that he leave, so she'd let him stay there till doomsday for all she cared. Climbing the stairs with all the dignity she could muster, she left him staring at her provocative backside.

Chapter Ten

"Naomi, I asked Ben for a status sheet on some contracts," Kate said, moving purposefully toward her secretary's desk. "You'd better give him a call. They should have been on my desk Friday." She glanced up idly from the list she was studying and caught the strange expression that flickered across Naomi's face.

"What's wrong?" she asked, frowning.

"I've already followed up on those status sheets," Naomi explained, "and Ben doesn't have them."

"Doesn't have them," Kate repeated blankly. "You mean he didn't finish them yet?"

Naomi's bright black gaze bounced off the obvious puzzlement in Kate's face. "Not exactly." She busied herself rearranging the articles on top of her desk. "He gave them to the boss."

Kate was almost accustomed to hearing Chase referred to as the boss, but her pulse still accelerated whenever his image took shape in her mind. But this time it wasn't from sexual excitement but from a slow burn that began somewhere in her chest and rose to tint her eyesight with a red haze.

"He gave them to the boss." Flatly, she repeated the words, the sheer lack of emotion a positive indication of the contained fury behind them.

She turned on her heel and closed the door of her office with a sharp snap. Rounding the desk, she sat down and reached for the telephone. She jabbed a series of numbers and tapped her fingers against the glass top of her desk, flattening her palm on the cold surface when Ben Scott answered.

"Ben, what's the story on those status sheets I requested?" She felt the wariness that crept into Ben's manner. "You didn't have any difficulty compiling the information, did you?" she inquired sweetly.

"Well, I . . ."

"Because my request was no different from dozens of similar requests from your staff over the past couple of years, Ben." She waited, her lips clamped in an angry line, her thoughts centered on Chase's arrogance as he moved in, usurping loyalties and overturning long-held practices without a by your leave.

"Let me come in there and talk to you, Kate," Ben offered quickly, and Kate could hear the unspoken message behind his suggestion. "Chase asked me—"

Kate didn't wait to hear anymore. She replaced the receiver quietly and rose from her chair with a determined grace. She strode past Naomi's desk without a word. Naomi's gray curls bobbed sympathetically as she watched her superior disappear down the hall.

Chase had retained the elderly secretary who had

served Kate's father for years, and that lady looked up with a pleasant smile of recognition and welcome.

"Miss Langford, how are you?" She reached for the intercom. "Just let me buzz Mr. Jamison and I'm sure you can go right on in."

Kate's lips stretched into the semblance of a smile without pausing and pushed open the door to Chase's office before the startled woman could react.

She halted just inside, the shield of her anger for once bringing some kind of protection against the sight of Chase and the sheer force of his attraction. He glanced up, only a slight narrowing of his eyes revealing his awareness of her and the obvious anger that tremored through her. His keen gaze noted the brightness of her eyes, her taut mouth, both hands clenched by her sides, all indications of a consuming rage. He rose slowly.

"Kate," he said, acknowledging her with a slight tilt of his dark brown head.

"Why did you intercept the status reports that I requested from Ben?" she began without preamble.

"Good morning," he said pleasantly. "Can I offer you some coffee?" The amused mockery in his manner only increased her fury.

She wrapped her arms around her middle, impatience glittering in her blue eyes while she battled an overwhelming desire to actually hit him.

"Don't patronize me, Chase," she snapped. "I want some answers!"

Indolently, he rounded the corner of his desk and drew up before her, resting one lean hip and muscular thigh on the corner of the massive desk, which served as a life-support center for what was now Langford Marine.

"You came for a showdown," he stated, his gaze running over the flushed features, pausing to stare interestingly at the rapidfire pulse in her throat.

"Why did you countermand my orders to Ben?" she repeated. "This is not the first time you have issued instructions which override something I have requested. I want to know why."

"I think you know why," he responded, quietly impersonal.

She frowned. "No, I don't."

He sighed with heavy patience. "You aren't running Langford anymore, Kate. While your father was alive, you did not exceed your authority by assuming more and more responsibility. After all, your father owned the business. But now I'm the owner, and your position is not one in which you need to become involved in the nitty-gritty." He scraped weary fingers against the back of his neck, and Kate noted the lines of fatigue near his mouth. He had worked all day Sunday and into the night, alongside the clean-up crews, clearing the debris of the storm and restoring order so that it was work as usual that day. He should have rested after that blow on the head, but no one had been able to get him to quit. She ignored the anxious concern that rose in her when she remembered the hours Saturday night when he had been in pain, contemptuous of her own weakness. Two minutes in his company and her anger was already dissipating.

"Chase," she began with a renewed effort to stick to the subject, "if you don't intend for me to become involved, then what is the point in my being at Langford's? Are you trying to get rid of me?"

A shuttered look entered his eyes. "Would you go?"

Her breath was released in a shocked hiss. "Would I go! For heaven's sake, Chase, this is my work. My grandfather established this business, and I'm the only Langford left in it. Is it so hard to accept that I want to remain a part of it?"

"Not a part of it, Kate. You want all of it." With

typical arrogance, he refused to allow her to express the indignation he could see in her face. "Don't fool yourself that I haven't been aware of your efforts to retain control, because I have."

He observed the abrupt loss of color in her face. "You are obstructive in numerous little ways, doing everything you can to complicate my life. Oh, nothing too blatant," he informed her grimly, "because open warfare might damage your precious image."

"You're crazy!"

"No, lady, I'm not crazy, but you are if you think I'm going to sit back and take it. I realize you are having difficulty accepting the changed circumstances, but the decisions at Langford's are made by me now, and that's the way it's going to be—it's a permanent arrangement." He paused, then added deliberately, "Or at least it is until I appoint a successor."

Her eyes slid away from his unwavering look, but a condemning rush of color stained her cheeks. The awful truth was that there was something in what he said. It had been difficult, almost impossible, she admitted ruefully, to relinquish the reins to Chase completely. She couldn't seem to overcome the sense of competition that existed between them. And now everything was even more complicated by her physical response to him. Her chin raised in a determined show of confidence.

"Is this what you mean by having a showdown?"

His gaze remained as steady as ever. "I've been patient, but no more. I know you, and I know your nature, Kate. If I hadn't brought it to a head by intercepting those reports, you would just keep on running the whole damn place. I know you're capable of making a shambles of my authority."

Her eyes dropped to her hands, tightly clenched in front of her. "You're wrong, but I know you won't believe me. You make it sound as if I wanted the business to fail. That's ridiculous."

"Not the business," he corrected quietly. "Just me. You wanted me to fail."

She was unable to meet his eyes; the accusation was too hard to take. There was something relentless about Chase. He was not a man who would accept defeat, but it was equally important to her to come out of this whole mess with some semblance of her professional life intact, because it was all too clear to Kate that her heart was lost to Chase. She drew her thoughts up shortly. What was she thinking? Victory and defeat were terms used in warfare. Did they apply in her relationship with Chase? Did she and Chase have a relationship? She wouldn't have thought so before Saturday night, but her instincts told her Chase wasn't indifferent to her.

She laughed shakily. "It sounds as though you are suggesting there is something personal in my reactions to you and your methods," she said in a tone that she hoped concealed the urgency she felt.

He leaned back complacently, but his eyes, narrowed on her face, were too perceptive. "And there's nothing personal in your grudge against me?"

"I don't have a grudge against you!" she denied indignantly. "Why do you keep on about that?" She paused, letting her eyes sweep over the powerful bulk of his frame, negligently at ease in the executive chair, his whole attitude that of a predator cat toying with a mouse. "In fact, if anyone could be accused of trespassing into personal territory, surely your behavior Saturday night qualifies."

"I assume you're referring to what I said to Mark Devereaux," he replied smoothly, "and not to anything that occurred between you and me."

She flushed but refused to be sidetracked. "That's right," she said with mounting confidence. "You had no right interfering the way you did. It looked bad enough with me half dressed and—"

He shrugged. "I don't see you suffering any great loss."

Kate gasped. "Why, you conceited— Whether I suffered any loss or not is none of your business! That's just what I'm saying. You deliberately misled Mark. You insinuated something that was totally untrue." Her voice dropped huskily. "You acted almost . . . almost proprietary, Chase, which you know is nonsense, and then you have the nerve to suggest that any retaliatory action on my part is in some way a personal assault."

She saw the tense flexing of Chase's jaw, suggesting that he was not as relaxed as his sprawled appearance would have her believe. "Don't take me for a fool, Kate. There was nothing retaliatory in your actions at work. You started your campaign long before I ever gave you any reason to retaliate. As for Devereaux, nothing would make me believe you feel any passion for him. If that were true, you wouldn't respond to me as you do."

Kate's indrawn breath was a combination of pain and humiliation. Why did Chase always know just how to wound her? She seemed unable to mask her reactions to him, but for him to ungallantly remind her of her weakness hurt. Her hands balled into tight fists at her side. "I've had just about enough of your insufferable remarks, Chase Jamison," she began with feeling, only to break off as the door, which had been slightly ajar, was pushed open.

"Hello, darling," said a breathlessly feminine voice. "I do hope I'm not interrupting anything."

Chase rose, the slight flicker of annoyance vanishing from his eyes so quickly that Kate wasn't sure it had ever existed. He extended a friendly hand toward Gina Hart, who entered the office as though assured that she would be welcome.

The sharp stab of jealousy was becoming almost familiar to Kate, but she had no intention of hanging around in some masochistic paralysis while Gina fawned over Chase. Chase, of course, had no intention of allowing her to escape. As she stepped toward the door, he was already around his desk, strong fingers grasping her wrist to halt her in her tracks.

"Gina"— Chase greeted the blonde with every evidence of pleasure—"I thought you were somewhere in the Caribbean."

Gina treated Chase to one of her feline smiles. "Oh, the Mastersons were forced to return to Houston," she pouted, the boredom in her voice at variance with the hungry light in her eyes as they roamed every inch of Chase's body. "They plan to resume the cruise in a few days, but I knew you would be longing for a change after so many weeks in this deadly place, so I told them to count me out." Once again, that slow smile. "Wasn't that a good idea, darling?"

Kate couldn't tell what Chase thought of Gina's idea, and she told herself she didn't care. Several impotent tugs failed to free her wrist from the autocratic hold that Chase had on it. As a result, she stood like a sulky teenager, forced to listen while they engaged in a sophisticated and brittle conversation. Kate's dark thoughts were interrupted by Gina's unsubtle effort to get rid of her.

"Chase, could we go somewhere and . . ." Gina flashed an eloquent glance toward Kate, her eyes dropping briefly to his hand, anchoring her to his side. "I didn't want to wait until you got back to Texas, so . . ."

For heaven's sake, Kate thought disgustedly, didn't the woman ever finish a sentence?

"Look, Mr. Jamison," Kate began forcefully, only to falter when Chase's eyes collided with hers, his look revealing just how ridiculous he considered her use of formal address. "We can finish our discussion when you have more time," she stated, ignoring the grim line of his jaw. She turned to Gina. "There is a unique little bar just minutes from here which I'm sure you will like. You and Chase can have all the privacy you require. It will relieve the tedium of his life here as well as freeing me for some real work. I've certainly got an overflowing in-basket waiting for me."

Let her mull that over, Kate thought with satisfaction, turning a defiant look on Chase, uncaring what interpretation his girl friend put on the undercurrents that vibrated with almost tangible force between the grim-visaged Chase and herself. He released her wrist with a slight inclination of his head, but she didn't make the mistake of thinking he conceded victory in that round. The glint in his eye hinted at a reckoning later, but Kate didn't wait around to find out. With what dignity she could muster, she left his office.

In the hours that followed, she had a lot of difficulty keeping her mind on her work. Although she denied it even to herself, she kept a surreptitious watch for Chase's return. Lunch came and went, and when he still had not put in an appearance, Kate's concentration completely deteriorated. She threw her pen down in disgust and turned her chair so that her gaze strayed to the window and beyond.

She was a fool to allow Gina's appearance to upset her. What was she to Chase? There had been an implied intimacy in her attitude. Was she his mistress? Were they engaged? A searing flame burned through her. She thought of her own awakened sexuality, the flames fanned by Chase's skill and mastery as a lover. But nothing he had done or said suggested he intended anything more than a casual affair. In all honesty, he had never even suggested an affair. His behavior could be that of any healthy, virile male away from home with a willing, not unattractive partner.

Kate's eyes closed weakly. How it hurt to think Chase's behavior toward her could be that casual when her own feelings were so intense. She swallowed hard around an obstruction in her throat. Was his interest merely the result of propinquity? He was so totally immersed in Langford's and the challenge of turning a faltering business around that to read anything more into his actions the few times they were alone was ridiculous. Even so, her foolish heart insisted, there could be no doubt he desired her. Recalling the passion that flared between them during the storm and his inexplicable behavior afterward when Mark had attempted to assert a prior claim to Kate's affection, she could make no sense of any of it.

And she had hardly endeared herself to Chase. His accusations held more than a grain of truth. Admitting now just exactly what she had been doing, Kate's motives were suddenly obvious. It came back to the same thing. When she was seventeen, she had needed recognition from Chase, and the mature Kate was unchanged. If she could not captivate him as a woman, then perhaps he would respond to her undenied ability as a businesswoman. Failing there, too, as Chase seemed to respond with only vague interest in her business acumen, she had then commenced a more negative campaign.

Well, she had certainly grabbed his attention with that tactic. And it proved he saw her only as an extension of her family's business. When she began complicating his life, he had taken notice, all right. Just as certainly as when she was seventeen, she had managed to convince Chase she was still as spoiled and capricious as ever.

Reaction vibrated through her. She lowered her

hands and stared unseeing when they fell listlessly to her lap. Would she never learn to curb her tempestuous nature as far as Chase was concerned?

She drew a shaky breath and rose. A glance at her desk revealed at least a dozen items that she could work on if only she could banish thoughts of Chase and Gina Hart. Since she couldn't, she decided to go home. After a couple of halfhearted attempts to straighten out the chaos of paper on her desk, she flipped the switch for the lights, plunging the office in midday gloom.

At the door, she drew back sharply. Chase's lean, powerful bulk nearly filled the door frame.

"Leaving early?" His calm gaze inspected her; keenly alert, she attempted to conceal the fact that his appearance after hours of futile waiting caught her off guard.

"If you have no objection," she returned shortly, anger and some other emotion that she was unwilling to identify causing a rush of blood in her veins.

"Since when has my opinion influenced your actions?" he countered quickly, stepping through the doorway and closing the door behind him.

"What do you want, Chase?" Now that he was actually there, she didn't want to see him. Pent-up feelings that had been building up inside her all day spilled over. "I was leaving for the day. Just because you have finally decided to put in an appearance doesn't mean the rest of us haven't been doing business as usual," she hurled sarcastically.

Chase glanced at his watch, his calm complacency unaffected. "You don't punch a time clock, Kate, and neither do I. Sit down for a minute and let me fill you in on some things I didn't get around to this morning." He flipped on the lights, ignoring her indignant face, and leaned against her desk, one muscled thigh swinging casually.

Realizing that to continue to bicker with him

would result in nothing, Kate drew a deep breath but refused to return to her chair, preferring to deal with Chase closer to eye level.

"What is it?" she asked him curtly, every line in her body showing how extremely reluctant she was to listen to anything he said.

"The board meets tomorrow," he began, running a leisurely eye over her, "and I would like for you to be there."

Kate's eyes dropped to her hands. The board of directors of Langford's was composed entirely of elderly men, or at least it had been. Under the new organization, that would change, but it hardly affect-ed her, she thought bitterly. Now that Chase owned the company, he would see that the board was comprised of individuals hand-picked by himself. So why did he want her there? She held her breath, waiting for what was next.

"I have nominated you to the board. I'm perfectly confident you will be accepted. I wanted you to know about it in case you got it in your head to act contrary and not show up for the meeting." He watched with sardonic amusement while Kate ab-sorbed the astonishing fact that one of her most sought after ambitions was about to be realized, but hard on the heels of that came the bitter certainty that it was probably only a sop to her that Chase had conceived to cushion his real motive. Did he want to relegate her to a position on the board and at the same time push her out of the vital job that involved her in the everyday operation of the company? That thought hurt, overriding the first rush of pleasure and pride that had been her immediate reaction to Chase's news.

She lifted indigo dark eyes accusingly. "It won't work, Chase."

His brows snapped together. "What are you talk-ing about?" He stared hard at her, his features grim.

She squared her shoulders, doggedly holding his gaze. "I can see through this ploy, so you needn't bother to deny it. You want to shove me into some dark corner of the office instead of ousting me completely. You plan to placate me with a position on the board where the only thing I'll ever have to do will probably be to serve coffee to those old geezers who haven't done anything constructive for Langford's for years that I can see. Since my grandfather died and stopped thinking for them, they've been more interested in playing golf than managing the company."

He moved away from the desk with lightning speed and gripped her arms, the steel-hard strength of his fingers biting deeply into the soft tissue. "What in the world do you want from me, woman?" He shook his head helplessly. "Why do I keep on trying? I might have known you would find some reason to throw this back in my face the way you've distrusted everything I've done since I got here." He shook her gently, restraint in the feel of his hands on her shoulders.

"Well, why are you doing this?" Kate asked, puzzled by the wry slant of his mouth. "Just because you are in a position to make magnanimous gestures doesn't mean that I have to accept them. You're right; I don't trust you. I don't think you are nominating me for the board because of my qualifications. I think it's part of your plan . . ." She choked a little under the dangerous gleam in Chase's eyes.

"What makes you think I've got a plan?" he growled, his grip on her arms disturbing her senses.

She shook her head, doubt suddenly creeping in to the formerly iron-clad opinion of his motive. The bitter anger of a moment before faded into a bewildered uncertainty.

"I don't really think you have a plan," she began,

her mouth vulnerable as she concentrated on keeping it firm. "Or at least nothing which will be detrimental to Langford Marine. I think you just want to get rid of me."

He shifted, his restless hands moving up and down on her arms. He eyed her from half-closed lids, the thickness of his lashes obscuring his expression. "Why should I want to get rid of you?" he asked, releasing her abruptly.

She thrust her fingers through her tawny hair, choosing her words carefully. "I don't know. Now that Ron is gone, maybe you feel the company would be better off with no ties to the past." She laughed shortly, humorlessly. "It would certainly be less trying for you if I weren't around."

He had been toying with her pen while she spoke, and he swung around, pinning her with a hard gaze. "That is your opinion, Kate. I've never given you any reason to think any such thing."

Completely baffled now, she chewed her lower lip nervously. "Well, you can't deny we have very little in common."

A speculative gleam entered his eye. "Oh? On the contrary, I think that we are amazingly in tune."

A tiny thrill danced through her veins, an inevitable response to the teasing quality that had suddenly entered his voice. "Yes, well . . . But that wasn't what I—"

"Surely you aren't suggesting we have anything else going for us?" he challenged, a lazy, sensual smile curling his mouth.

Unwilling to admit how easily he could unnerve her, she lifted her chin, controlling the vulnerable movement of her mouth with an effort. "You know the answer to that as well as I." She made the noncommittal reply huskily.

"Because outside of our work at Langford's, there is only one other common bond between us. Right,

Kate?" Chase persisted, reinforcing his arguments with seductive mastery. His gaze drifted to her mouth, and Kate tried to resist the compelling force of her own response. It was only a momentary pause, because he reached for her and pulled her body, unresisting, close against him. He tilted her face toward his, his mouth hovering a whisper away while her eyes closed, shutting out everything except the feel of his arms, the male scent of him, the stimuli that triggered her own answering desire.

"If you're honest, Kate, you'll admit we have a lot in common." His lips moved feather light against her cheek, nuzzling the sensitive skin under her jaw.

"No," she insisted weakly, "it's just . . ."

He breathed warmly against the corner of her mouth, and she turned her head to try and elude his sensual attack. The line of her throat was being thoroughly investigated by his marauding tongue, and Kate's head spun dizzily, almost insensible under the sweet torture.

"We have this going for us, Kate. Why do you try to deny it?"

She moaned, sick because he was right and she was so powerless to resist him. One part of her mind urged restraint, but another more primitive, not-to-be-denied part of her blazed with an elemental desire for him. A victim of her love, she sighed in wordless surrender. Her arms slipped around his neck, her hands going eagerly into the sensuous thickness of his hair. His mouth against her own was a warm, wonderful instrument of pleasure, and a delicious languor spread throughout her body, boneless and pliant in his arms.

Kate gave no thought to where they were. That anyone might walk into her office and find her completely abandoned in a passionate embrace with Chase did not even cross her mind.

When he released her mouth and turned his lips

into the tangle of her hair, she felt his breath ragged and unsteady. She knew again with a woman's insight that he desired her, that he was as aroused as she, and joy flared inside her at the knowledge. She turned her face into the hard strength of his neck, inhaling deeply and happily.

But then she stiffened as the alien scent that clung to his clothes penetrated her dazed mind. The sweet, cloying fragrance was as effective as ice water to cool her ardor. It was the same scent that Gina Hart had worn that morning.

Suddenly, violently, Kate jerked away from Chase, startling him so that his brows drew together darkly and he frowned thunderously. "What is it now, Kate?" he demanded, refusing to remove hands that tightened around her waist when she would have pulled free.

"Isn't one woman enough for you, Chase?" Fiercely, she raked at his fingers, and reluctantly, he released her, a heavy passion still smoldering in his eyes.

"Wasn't Gina accommodating enough, or do you have some perverted idea of comparing the two of us?"

God, was there no limit to her stupidity? Kate dashed a hand across her eyes. It would be the final humiliation to cry now.

"What's the matter, Kate? Are you jealous?" he taunted, running furious eyes over her distressed features. "Haven't you been comparing my technique with Mark Devereaux's?"

No! she screamed silently, because no other man could ever come close to evoking from her the response Chase aroused with the slightest touch.

"But no matter," Chase persisted, not deterred by the stricken look she could not conceal. "We can discuss Gina Hart another time. Right now I want your word that you'll be at that meeting tomorrow at ten."

She threw him a bitter look. "You could have secured my cooperation in a less reprehensible way, Chase. You're right. I can't deny the attraction between us, but I think you're despicable to use it to gain your own ends."

She began to straighten her clothes, her dignity in shreds, the blue of her eyes overbright. She threw him a defiant look. "I don't have any apologies to make for my feelings. At least they're honest and spontaneous. And while we're on the subject, Mark Devereaux and I do not share an intimate relationship, whatever you may choose to believe. I couldn't compare your techniques even if so depraved an idea had ever occurred to me." The rush of tears to her eyes blurred her vision, so that Chase's body, tensely still, was only a watery outline. "But you . . . You're still the harsh taskmaster you were years ago when you chose to teach me a lesson. Still employing the same techniques calculated to make me feel cheap and promiscuous." She dashed a hand across her eyes, saw the bones clench in Chase's jaw and watched the color recede, leaving his features harshly defined. He reached for her.

"Kate, you've got it all wrong."

She flinched, moving with vulnerable grace away from him. "I'll be at the board meeting tomorrow morning, Chase, not because of any persuading you may have done, but because I'm a Langford and this company still means a lot to me."

She turned on her heel and left him without a backward glance.

Chapter Eleven

Olivia Langford climbed reluctantly into the car, directing one last anxious look into the pale features of her granddaughter. "I can still cancel this visit, Kate. I don't like leaving you under the circumstances."

Kate conjured up a smile. "I insist, Livvy. And you should get a move on; otherwise, you will catch the rush-hour traffic in New Orleans. Have a good time and don't worry about me."

Watching the car disappear around the curve of the drive, Kate held on to her smile grimly. When the sound of the car faded completely, she dropped the rigid composure she had maintained around her grandmother. Tears, held at bay since the board meeting that morning, rushed to her burning eyes, spilling over and pouring down her cheeks.

For a moment, she did nothing to stem the flow, staring blindly toward the calm surface of the Gulf, visible through the branches of a live oak. A gull's harsh cry echoed the misery of her heart. Disappointment and pain were a bitter taste in her mouth. Chase, the only person alive who had the power to wound her so mortally, had done so, and she was devastated by the ruthlessness of his action.

She stood there a few more minutes, indulging in uncharacteristic self-pity; then, squaring her shoulders and wiping the tears from her cheeks, she wandered back into the house. She couldn't forget the awful consequences of the board meeting, but she could refuse to let herself sink into a futile depression over it. But the sense of stunned shock remained in spite of her attempts to come to grips with Chase's latest maneuver.

The meeting had commenced that morning as planned. Chase appeared on schedule, flanked by three strangers, who, like Chase, reeked of corporate power and high finance. She was familiar with the regular group that comprised Langford's board of directors and assumed, correctly, as it turned out, that the three younger men were Chase's associates from his Texas headquarters.

After Chase had dispatched each item of business efficiently, Kate heard her own appointment put before the board and passed with no argument. Who would dare argue with Chase Jamison? To Kate's eyes, he was a near stranger exuding self-confidence and leashed power. He was in his element, chairing the board meeting as though he had been born there.

Politely, she had accepted the murmured congratulations from the board members, whose expressions masked their true reactions to having a woman trespass upon the hallowed realm of the board. Surprisingly, Chase's three associates reacted warmly to her appointment, and she felt herself thawing slightly under their combined good wishes.

But her satisfaction hadn't lasted very long. Shock

and dismay held her motionless as she heard Chase announce his resignation and intent to return to Texas to resume his demanding role as corporate boss. Of course she had known that Chase wouldn't be in Baytown forever, but she had resolutely refused to think about the time when he would leave. Her only comfort lay in the fact that she could retrieve the reins of control at Langford Marine, but even that was not destined to be. Chase went on to announce smoothly that Ben Scott was his choice as the new general manager of Langford's.

It was the last straw. The rest of the meeting passed for Kate in a blur of pain and anger and humiliation. Not that she didn't think Ben could handle the top job. If ever she had allowed herself to consider the possibility, in all fairness, she would have to agree that he qualified on all counts. But she had really wanted that job. If she couldn't have Chase, couldn't have a future with him, then she needed the challenge and sheer time-consuming effort that it would take to be general manager. Valiantly, she tried to swallow the deep disappointment that missing out on the appointment brought. She knew with absolute certainty that she was more than qualified to hold the job, too. In fact, while her father was alive, she had actually functioned in the position that Chase was now handing to Ben Scott. Leaving her with . . . what?

She slammed the refrigerator door after a depressed examination of its contents. Food had no appeal for her even though she lectured herself on the stupidity of allowing Chase's actions to affect her beyond the limits of good sense.

She wandered upstairs, rejecting an inclination to lounge in a warm tub. It seemed a melancholy thing to do, and she was trying to overcome depression, not foster it, she told herself. So after a brisk shower, she pulled a jewel-blue silk Japanese-style kimono out of her closet and slipped into it. The vivid color deepened the indigo of her eyes, and she brushed her tawny hair into a tumbled mass on her shoulders. Meeting her own gaze in the mirror, she realized the deep ache was still present, but her resilient nature had reasserted itself, and some of the pain had eased a little.

When the front door chimes sounded, she grimaced slightly, hardly in the mood for company. As she headed for the door, a loud, impatient knocking replaced the melodious chimes.

Suddenly, Kate knew who was at the door. Her hands went defensively to the sash of her kimono, and she pulled the knot more securely around her waist, sliding her palms down slim, silk-clad thighs. She inhaled slowly and reached for the door.

She pulled it open, watching the shaft of light that illuminated the rough-hewn features of Chase's face. One arm was still raised, but he lowered it slowly, his gaze locked with hers.

"What do you want, Chase?" She held the door open, deliberately ignoring the silent appeal in his look.

"Am I still welcome at Fox Briar?" The wry inflection caught at her breath, undermining her resolve to treat him with a cold politeness that negated the attraction surging between them. Even after his betrayal, she was still drawn irresistibly toward Chase as to no other man.

She stepped back, motioning him inside. His suit jacket was slung over one shoulder, and his tie had been loosened along with the collar button on his shirt. He looked tired and drawn, and beneath the harsh light of the hall chandelier, she thought she detected an unusual hesitancy about him.

"Whatever you came for, Chase, say it and then

go," she said coolly. "As you can see, I'm not dressed for visitors."

As though her remark was intended to invite his inspection, he raked an appraising eye over her heightened features and down to her throat, where one hand hovered nervously. To dispel the tension heightening between them, she turned her back and closed the door, fighting the trembling awareness she always felt when he looked at her. Holding her breath, she waited, and when he still said nothing, she gathered enough nerve to face him.

"You disappeared after the board meeting." A muscle worked at the side of his mouth, and he turned impatiently, tossing his jacket carelessly onto a chair.

She lifted her chin, averting her face from the keen scrutiny of his gaze. "I suddenly lost all desire for work."

Something flared briefly in his eyes, then was quickly gone. "I'm relieved. Given your usual attitude, I wouldn't have been surprised if you had immediately launched a campaign to sabotage Ben."

Speechless with hurt, she stared at him.

"You could, you know. Easy enough." He raked restless fingers through his hair. "Hell, Kate, that's not what I'm here for." He looked around as if only then becoming aware of his surroundings. "Where's Olivia?"

"Out." Still smarting from the injustice of his remark about Ben, she didn't bother making her reply civil.

He made a move to go around her, hooking two fingers behind the loosened knot of his tie and pulling it completely off.

"Where are you going?"

"May I have a drink?" Fatigue bracketed his mouth, and his usual vitality was missing. "It has been a long day," he said, unbuttoning his shirt and baring the tanned muscles of his neck and a broad expanse of chest hair.

Kate found herself directing him toward a cabinet where the liquor supply was kept while she removed a glass and slid it across the counter.

She watched while he poured straight scotch into the glass and tossed it off in one swallow. Immediately, he refilled the empty glass and lifted it.

"Did you come here tonight to get drunk?" Kate asked, sarcasm and a crazy concern warring in her mind.

He eyed the contents of the drink ruefully. "What I came for isn't easy, but we're overdue for some straight talk, and tonight's the night." As though gauging her reaction, he raised his eyes to hers, his gaze almost challenging.

"We have nothing to discuss, Chase," she said bleakly. "You said it all this morning. You've succeeded in everything you set out to do. What's the point in dragging it all out with a lot of meaningless dialogue? You've more than revenged yourself against my family. Everything that once bore the name of Langford is now yours. I hope you're satisfied."

Bitterly, she turned her head, averting her face so that he would not see the tears that blurred her sight or suspect the aching longing that burned inside her to have him comfort her in her distress. She was appalled herself that in the midst of her pain she should seek comfort from the perpetrator of it all.

"I'm not satisfied, Kate," he said quietly, his expression sober. "Everything that bears the name Langford is not mine."

Confused she stared at him. "But you—"

"You're not mine."

White-faced, she sank onto the sofa. "That's not funny."

She heard him swear as he sat down beside her,

studying her with a hard intensity. "I'm not trying to be funny. I gave Ben Scott that job because I didn't want you to have it."

"Tell me about it," she snapped acidly.

His mouth compressed angrily, but he let her remark pass. "I knew that if you had it, you would never leave here."

Kate frowned now in total confusion. "But why would that matter to you?" Her dark blue gaze studied his lean features.

"I wanted you to be free to come with me."

To come with him? Kate's heart leaped with joy, but immediately she remembered Gina Hart. She had been rejected by Chase before. She would not be guilty of assuming anything where he was concerned. She moistened her dry lips, swallowing to quiet the roaring in her ears.

"You mean there's a job for me on your corporate staff?"

Chase's back was to her, but at her words, he turned to stare at her, his expression a mixture of angry exasperation and impatience. "My staff?" He laughed shortly. "Not exactly."

A cold chill settled somewhere near the region of her heart. She rose from the sofa, a proud lift to her chin. "Are you suggesting an affair?"

Going suddenly still, he stared at her, guarded speculation in his eyes. "Would you agree if I were?"

There it was. Kate's heart thudded wildly. Disjointed thoughts flashed like quicksilver in her mind. If it was all she could ever have, she knew she wanted to grab the chance. If it was the only way she would ever claim a part of Chase, even if it lasted only a few months, or weeks, she wanted it. How long did the average affair last, she wondered desolately. Could she conceal her true feelings from him? Not for anything could she let him know how completely, hopelessly, she loved him.

His eyes, as he watched her, were a deep, fathomless brown. With one hand, he stroked the side of her face. "Decisions, decisions," he murmured, rubbing his thumb sensuously across her lips.

"Chase, I . . ."

One hand traveled down the silken contours of her arm and waist and hips in the kimono. "You don't have anything on under this thing," he said thickly, dropping both hands to the sash and disposing of it in one urgent tug.

The kimono fell away, leaving her exposed to his dark, hungry gaze. She heard the sharply indrawn breath he made as his eyes lingered on her breasts as they swelled in anticipation of his touch, their dusky rose tips taut, pebble hard. Darkly turbulent, his eyes moved up to hers, and wordlessly, for a timeless moment, they were content just to gaze at each other. Then, as his head descended, Kate sought the heaven of his lips, eager to taste him, to savor the essence of this man whom she desired above all others. The kiss deepened as he explored the soft inside hollows of her mouth, his hands gentle on her arms and at her back.

He lifted his lips the scant inch that separated them. "I need you so much, Kate," he said urgently, his breath filling her mouth, stealing her soft sigh. "It's driving me crazy, being near you every day, telling myself it won't kill me if I have to leave you."

His hands slipped beneath her, lifting and settling her comfortably into his complementing male contours. Dazed by his seductive voice, rocked by the caress of his breath at her ear, Kate was swept away beyond coherent thought.

She floated in a sweet languor when he swung her into his arms and carried her over to the sofa. He laid her down and then settled his own length over her, satisfyingly heavy against her femininity. His eyes roved over her rosy features, one hand coming

up to gently entwine the tawny swirl of her hair,
spread out on the cushions. Then his hands began a
slow, delicious exploration of her body, provoking
little sounds from her throat as she moved restlessly,
seeking the complete satisfaction her senses craved.
This was where she belonged, her heart sang. Could
her instincts be wrong? She rejected that thought as
quickly as it formed, pushing doubt and uncertainty
deep in the back of her mind, wanting nothing to
intrude on the wonder of this moment. At last, she
felt free to shed her inhibitions in Chase's arms, to
give rein to her need to express emotions too long
held in check.

Through the barrier of his clothes, her hands
moved wonderingly over the long, sinewy muscles of
his shoulders. She thrilled when his body went taut,
then trembled beneath her inexperienced yet eager
fingers. Chase's passion was now mounting steadily,
and his mouth moved erotically over her flesh, his
moist lips closing warmly over the throbbing peak of
one breast. A wild longing became a driving need for
fulfillment, compelling Kate to reply in kind, to
touch Chase as he stroked and caressed her, to
satisfy the tingling in her fingers, to explore his body
with the same freedom he used to delight her.

"Darling Kate, beautiful Kate," he murmured
thickly, the rough texture of his tongue grazing her
sensitized flesh, sweeping up along the arched line of
her throat, seeking and finding with unerring accuracy her parted lips, plunging hungrily to feed insatiably on the honeyed sweetness inside. His hands were
all over her, sweeping down her rib cage, following
the curving line of her hips, stroking restlessly the
length of her thighs. When her hands pushed fever-
ishly inside his shirt and pulled it away to gain access
to his chest, he raised slightly and shrugged it off,
slinging it aside, then drawing her against him while

she gloried in the strange, sweet sensation of the abrasive scrape of his masculine skin against her own smooth nudity.

Wildly aroused now, Kate longed only for total fulfillment. She sank her nails into Chase's shoulders in wordless demand, and he lifted his head to look into her eyes, indigo dark with passion, her love-soft features flushed and vulnerable.

An answering blaze of desire flared in his own eyes as his gaze, dark with anticipation, seared over her.

She nearly cried out when he hesitated, his breathing harsh and uneven.

"No! This is not—"

As she watched, a savage frustration contorted his features, replacing passion, and he swung up and away from her, his shoulders heaving as though he had been running. "This is not what I want, Kate."

Dazed, passion momentarily checked, Kate could only lie motionless while her bewildered mind sought some reason for Chase's abrupt rejection. She stared at his broad back, watching while he drew deep, shuddering breaths to control the desire she knew still raged in his body. She was no complete innocent. He had been fully aroused, only moments from consummating that desire, and she, God help her, had offered no resistance. So why was he now standing a safe ten feet across the room from her?

"I love you, Kate."

She sat up, groping for the blue kimono. "What?"

He turned, his face pale. The rugged planes, starkly defined, clenched with some emotion she couldn't identify. "I said, I love you," he repeated, then laughed shortly, humorlessly. "I've been trying to tell you since yesterday."

She was still for a second; then her hands came alive, jerking the kimono into place, belting it savagely. "And that's supposed to explain what just happened?" she flashed bitterly. "You'll have to excuse me if I fail to be amused, Chase. Somehow your behavior just doesn't fit the image of a man in love." She saw the broad shoulders flex as lean fingers appeared to rub wearily the back of his neck.

"I didn't mean us to . . . What I intended . . ." He floundered helplessly, and Kate rushed into the breach.

"Just exactly what did you intend?"

He turned, meeting her gaze levelly. "I wanted to arouse you to the point that you would do anything I asked."

"Why you despicable—" Nearly incoherent, Kate could only stare while Chase's skin took on a ruddy hue, but he grimly held her gaze.

"It's not what you think, Kate. I've always known I held some kind of sexual attraction for you, but that kind of relationship will never satisfy me."

"What kind of relationship?" she asked through stiff lips, convinced she would never hurt quite so deeply ever again.

Chase began a restless prowl about the room, his brows fiercely drawn. "I tried hard to resist you when you were seventeen, Kate. The temptation was strong to take what you were so eager to give, but you were too young to know your mind, and I was able to hold off, at least until that night. I never should have gotten into the car with you." He stopped pacing, slanting a wry look at her. "I almost succumbed to the attraction I had been fighting for months. That was when I knew I should get away before something happened which you might regret later. I knew I would never regret making love to you."

Kate could hardly concentrate under the range of emotions that assailed her. Confusion and astonishment held her stock-still, while a heady delight

began to warm the chill that had set in when Chase
had withdrawn from her only moments before.

"The theft of the prototype plans seemed a fateful
occurrence, providing the impetus I needed to do
the wise thing." His mouth quirked in a self-derisive
movement. "I probably never would have found the
strength to leave otherwise." He looked into her
features, incredulous and pale as she listened. "You
were beautiful and innocent, and I longed to be the
man to teach you about love. Under the circumstances, I figured you would forget me soon
enough."

"So you left and never gave me another thought."
She flung the words at him, the bitter loss of those
long-ago years lacing the tremor in her voice. How
many countless hours had she filled with his image
during those empty days and weeks after he left.

"I thought of you often. Once, while I was in a
conference in California, I ran into Phillip." His eyes
flicked to hers, the beginning of a gleam catching at
her breath. "Actually, I looked him up. He told me
you had already completed one year toward your
degree, and he was full of fatherly love and pride as
he ticked off your accomplishments."

"Did he tell you I was with him in San Francisco?"

His eyes were steady on hers. "Yes. I wanted to
see you, but I felt I should tell him a little of what
had happened that night. He was surprised, a little
shocked, I think. He said perhaps it would be best to
give you some time, allow you an opportunity to
finish your education." His gaze strayed from her
face, wandering over the objects in the room without
really seeing them. "I may have overreacted, but I
thought he was tactfully warning me off. I owed him
my education and the basis of my professional
training. I could hardly do less than honor his
feelings." His eyes sought hers again. "A few

months ago, he called and asked if I would be interested in Langford Marine. That same day, I ran a check of the business. My advisers thought I was crazy when I disregarded their opinions and made an offer to Phillip before he could change his mind."

She was still reeling from the incredible things she was hearing from Chase. "Why did you arrange my appointment to the board?"

"I wanted you to have a vital part in your family's company," he replied immediately, without a moment's hesitation. "It's your rightful heritage."

"But I couldn't handle the job as general manager?" Her eyes darkened with remembered pain.

He was still, taut with some leashed emotion. "Not on top of all your other responsibilities."

Her mouth was bitter. "What other responsibilities?"

"Your responsibilities as my wife," he declared, his sherry-brown eyes looking into hers.

Her heart leaped in her throat; a delicious warm happiness spread inside her, flowering like azaleas in the sun. "But why did you stop just now?" she asked, cautiously restraining a wild impulse to fall into his arms. "You could have taken me. It wasn't necessary to offer marriage." She held her breath for his reply.

"It was necessary. Nothing else will satisfy me." He shot her a knowing look. "I'm not going to settle for a brief fling just to satisfy the attraction you feel for me. I want more than that. I want to start and end the day with you. I want to sleep with you and wake up with you. I want to eat breakfast as well as dinner with you. I love you, Kate! What will it take to convince you?" One hand sliced through the air as he drew up to a window and leaned an arm against the frame, staring blindly outside.

Tentatively, almost afraid to believe she had just

been handed her heart's desire, Kate advanced toward him, eying his broad back, thrilling to the line of his narrow hips and strong, muscular legs. She reached out and touched him, feeling the instant taut response.

Chase turned, studying her with an intensity that brought her heart up into her throat. She smiled, her look filled with an incredulous joy. "Is this real?" she whispered on a note of wonder.

His hands came up to frame her face. "Everything I did you greeted with suspicion and doubt," he informed her, the frustration he had suffered vibrating in his voice. "The only thing right between us was your response when I took you in my arms."

She drew a shaky breath, her hands anchoring at his waist. "Oh, Chase."

He tilted his head, his gaze measuring, but a lazy sensuality gleamed in his eyes. "Oh, Chase?" he mimicked softly.

She laughed suddenly and joyfully, and his mouth swooped to capture the sound and stayed to plunder the sweetness of her surrender.

"I love you, Chase," she whispered against his throat. "I have since I was twelve."

"Oh, God, it's the same for me," he whispered into her hair, his arms enfolding her, holding her in fierce possession. "I don't remember when I didn't love you."

She sighed, bestowing a fervent kiss on the side of his mouth, her arms tightly clasped around his neck. His dark head bent, nuzzling aside the folds of blue silk, and Kate felt the ready rise of her own response as he sought the delicate swell of one taut crest.

She spoke shakily, her eyes dreamy. "I was so sure you just wanted Langford Marine. I wouldn't dare let myself believe you could want me."

"I'm prepared to spend a lot of time convincing

you," he growled, his lips wreaking havoc along the line of her throat, exploring the contours of her ear.

Finally, a flushed and trembling Kate leaned back against his arms, her eyes lustrous and glowing. "Could I ask you something?"

Chase nodded, thrilling her with the tenderness in his eyes when she realized it was for her only.

"Where did Gina Hart fit in your life?"

He captured a strand of her hair, glinting dark gold in the lamplight. "Gina and I have some mutual friends," he stated confidently, no hint of reluctance about him. "And that's it. There has never been anything between us."

"I thought she was your fiancée or maybe even your mistress."

He laughed, tucking her sun-streaked head into the curve of his shoulder. "Didn't you say that was the role I was reserving for you?"

She nipped the naked flesh of his arm, looking gratified when he winced. "You knew what I was thinking, and you didn't even try to explain!"

Tipping up her chin, he dropped a hard, sensual kiss on her mouth. "I'll try to make it up to you," he promised, and the fire of her response destroyed any doubt that lingered.

"I wanted to believe my instincts," Kate began pensively, "but you never gave me any idea that I might have a place in your future. I was even beginning to consider seducing you. At least I would have you for a little while."

His head tilted, a satisfied smile curling his mouth. "It's a good thing I couldn't read your mind, although after spending one whole night with you, I knew I wanted you forever." He kissed the corner of her mouth tenderly. "It felt so right."

She turned her face into his chest. "It felt right to me, too. My feelings for you as a seventeen-year-old had multiplied a thousand times. I knew how much I loved you when I saw you lying unconscious on the deck of that ship."

"I began to think I might have a chance with you when you took such good care of me that night. But earlier that afternoon when I invited you for dinner, I certainly didn't feel too confident." His mouth twisted wryly. "I had been talking with Olivia when you walked in, all wind tossed and looking like a sexy dream girl, but the air fairly crackled with the hostile vibrations you directed my way. All of a sudden, I wanted to reduce that superior, queenly, cool façade you maintained to quivering submission. I knew I could, too. I just didn't know whether I could handle taking you and then forgetting it if you were just fooling around. I had an idea even then that a lifetime with you might not be long enough."

Her hand spread over the rippled surface of his chest. "I couldn't figure out why you invited me. You were so nonchalant that I wondered if you might need someone to fill a boring Saturday night," she accused, then laughing with him when she felt his smile against her cheek. "And later you purposely led Mark to think the worst. I was totally confused by then."

Chase's smile disappeared. "I intended to eliminate him," he said on a hard, clipped note. "I could tell he wanted you, and I couldn't stand idly by and watch. He had had his chance. It was my turn."

She tucked her head gently under his chin, nestling against the warm, secure wall of his chest. "There was never anything between Mark and me."

Tension flexed briefly in his arms, letting her know the extent of his claim. "I apologize for those stupid remarks I made about your relationship with him, darling. I was trying to deal with jealousy for the first time in my life, and it wasn't pleasant."

"It's all right now. I wanted to tell you many times, but you always made me so mad that I told myself you didn't deserve an explanation. Besides, I was too busy telling myself I didn't care about your opinion of me."

"People in love can be pretty dense," Chase said philosophically.

She smiled, sliding one palm over the rough mat of hair on his chest, her bones almost melting in a rush of love for him. "Are you going to give me a staff position?" she teased. "After all, it's all your fault that I missed out as general manager of Langford's this morning."

"Until we start a family," Chase affirmed generously, most of his attention devoted to the tantalizing glimpse of cleavage revealed at the neckline of the kimono.

Kate's pulse leaped as his hand slipped warmly over one firm breast, and she savored the delight of knowing her body pleased him as much as she delighted in the sheer male sexuality of his. She slid her fingers through the thick texture of his hair. "I love you so much, Chase. All of my life, it seems."

He looked up, his gaze dark and intense. "You are everything I've ever wanted in a woman. I love you in every way it's possible to love. And now that you're mine, I can't describe how happy I am."

"It's all so wonderful," Kate said on a note of sheer incredulity. "I never knew. I thought that cool, almost mocking attitude meant you thought of me as the spoiled brat you accused me of being eight years ago."

Tenderly, he touched the side of her mouth with his lips. "No chance," he whispered, trailing kisses across her cheek, his caressing hands promising ecstasy beyond anything she had ever dreamed. "I was thinking how much I wanted to do this . . . and this . . ."

She trembled with growing anticipation, and for the second time Chase consigned the blue kimono to the floor. Cool silk was replaced by warm hands that thrilled and excited everywhere they touched. A mounting desire, gripping them both, demanded fulfillment.

Suddenly, he swung her up into his arms, pausing to bestow one more drugging kiss before striding for the massive curved stairs. He searched her face, his breath stirring the hair at her temples. "I've always fancied carrying you up these stairs and making mad love to you throughout the night."

She wrapped her arms securely around his neck, nestling against him contentedly. "That's funny, I've always had that same fantasy, ever since the first time I saw you mowing the grass without your shirt."

"Brazen wench," he said, chuckling, his eyes alight as he studied her with an appreciative grin.

"Of course," she went on nonchalantly, "I was too young to know the particulars, but I planned to have you fill me in."

He was at the top of the stairs. "It's never too late," he promised, his lips hovering a fraction away from hers. "Where's your room?"

"Second on the left," she answered, straining to claim the sensual mouth, just out of reach.

He stepped into her room. "When is Olivia coming home?"

She settled back, smiling slowly, provocatively. "In three days."

He murmured something incoherent, his eyes flaring hungrily as he claimed her mouth in a hard, almost desperate kiss. "I don't know if that's long enough," he groaned as she surged against him in age-old demand.

"Then shouldn't we get started?"

One foot raised and gently, firmly, kicked the door closed.

Silhouette Romance

IT'S YOUR OWN SPECIAL TIME
Contemporary romances for today's women.
Each month, six very special love stories will be yours
from SILHOUETTE.

$1.75 each

☐ 100 Stanford
☐ 101 Hardy
☐ 102 Hastings
☐ 103 Cork
☐ 104 Vitek
☐ 105 Eden
☐ 106 Dailey
☐ 107 Bright
☐ 108 Hampson
☐ 109 Vernon
☐ 110 Trent
☐ 111 South
☐ 112 Stanford
☐ 113 Browning
☐ 114 Michaels
☐ 115 John
☐ 116 Lindley
☐ 117 Scott
☐ 118 Dailey
☐ 119 Hampson
☐ 120 Carroll
☐ 121 Langan
☐ 122 Scofield
☐ 123 Sinclair
☐ 124 Beckman
☐ 125 Bright
☐ 126 St. George

☐ 127 Roberts
☐ 128 Hampson
☐ 129 Converse
☐ 130 Hardy
☐ 131 Stanford
☐ 132 Wisdom
☐ 133 Rowe
☐ 134 Charles
☐ 135 Logan
☐ 136 Hampson
☐ 137 Hunter
☐ 138 Wilson
☐ 139 Vitek
☐ 140 Erskine
☐ 142 Browning
☐ 143 Roberts
☐ 144 Goforth
☐ 145 Hope
☐ 146 Michaels
☐ 147 Hampson
☐ 148 Cork
☐ 149 Saunders
☐ 150 Major
☐ 151 Hampson
☐ 152 Halston
☐ 153 Dailey
☐ 154 Beckman

☐ 155 Hampson
☐ 156 Sawyer
☐ 157 Vitek
☐ 158 Reynolds
☐ 159 Tracy
☐ 160 Hampson
☐ 161 Trent
☐ 162 Ashby
☐ 163 Roberts
☐ 164 Browning
☐ 165 Young
☐ 166 Wisdom
☐ 167 Hunter
☐ 168 Carr
☐ 169 Scott
☐ 170 Ripy
☐ 171 Hill
☐ 172 Browning
☐ 173 Camp
☐ 174 Sinclair
☐ 175 Jarrett
☐ 176 Vitek
☐ 177 Dailey
☐ 178 Hampson
☐ 179 Beckman
☐ 180 Roberts
☐ 181 Terrill

☐ 182 Clay
☐ 183 Stanley
☐ 184 Hardy
☐ 185 Hampson
☐ 186 Howard
☐ 187 Scott
☐ 188 Cork
☐ 189 Stephens
☐ 190 Hampson
☐ 191 Browning
☐ 192 John
☐ 193 Trent
☐ 194 Barry
☐ 195 Dailey
☐ 196 Hampson
☐ 197 Summers
☐ 198 Hunter
☐ 199 Roberts
☐ 200 Lloyd
☐ 201 Starr
☐ 202 Hampson
☐ 203 Browning
☐ 204 Carroll
☐ 205 Maxam
☐ 206 Manning
☐ 207 Windham

IT'S YOUR OWN SPECIAL TIME

Contemporary romances for today's women.
Each month, six very special love stories will be yours
from SILHOUETTE. Look for them wherever books are sold
or order now from the coupon below.

$1.95 each

☐ 208 Halston	☐ 228 King	☐ 248 St. George	☐ 268 Hunter
☐ 209 LaDame	☐ 229 Thornton	☐ 249 Scofield	☐ 269 Smith
☐ 210 Eden	☐ 230 Stevens	☐ 250 Hampson	☐ 270 Camp
☐ 211 Walters	☐ 231 Dailey	☐ 251 Wilson	☐ 271 Allison
☐ 212 Young	☐ 232 Hampson	☐ 252 Roberts	☐ 272 Forrest
☐ 213 Dailey	☐ 233 Vernon	☐ 253 James	☐ 273 Beckman
☐ 214 Hampson	☐ 234 Smith	☐ 254 Palmer	☐ 274 Roberts
☐ 215 Roberts	☐ 235 James	☐ 255 Smith	☐ 275 Browning
☐ 216 Saunders	☐ 236 Maxam	☐ 256 Hampson	☐ 276 Vernon
☐ 217 Vitek	☐ 237 Wilson	☐ 257 Hunter	☐ 277 Wilson
☐ 218 Hunter	☐ 238 Cork	☐ 258 Ashby	☐ 278 Hunter
☐ 219 Cork	☐ 239 McKay	☐ 259 English	☐ 279 Ashby
☐ 220 Hampson	☐ 240 Hunter	☐ 260 Martin	☐ 280 Roberts
☐ 221 Browning	☐ 241 Wisdom	☐ 261 Saunders	☐ 281 Lovan
☐ 222 Carroll	☐ 242 Brooke	☐ 262 John	☐ 282 Halldorson
☐ 223 Summers	☐ 243 Saunders	☐ 263 Wilson	☐ 283 Payne
☐ 224 Langan	☐ 244 Sinclair	☐ 264 Vine	☐ 284 Young
☐ 225 St. George	☐ 245 Trent	☐ 265 Adams	☐ 285 Gray
☐ 226 Hamson	☐ 246 Carroll	☐ 266 Trent	
☐ 227 Beckman	☐ 247 Halldorson	☐ 267 Chase	

SILHOUETTE BOOKS, Department SB/1

1230 Avenue of the Americas
New York, NY 10020

Please send me the books I have checked above. I am enclosing $_____ (please add 75¢ to cover postage and handling. NYS and NYC residents please add appropriate sales tax). Send check or money order—no cash or C.O.D's please. Allow six weeks for delivery.

NAME _____

ADDRESS _____

CITY _____ STATE/ZIP _____

Silhouette **Romance**

Coming Next Month

The Man From the Past by Dorothy Cork

Ferris never dreamed that the dark, compelling cousin of the
man she once loved would be the one to conquer her heart. Now
Cleve proposed a marriage of convenience to save her beloved
winery. But Ferris longed for a marriage in every
sense of the word.

Permanent Fixture by Janet Joyce

Megan knew that her new job as executive secretary to the
president would be a challenge. But she didn't think she'd have
to fight her attraction for her new boss—especially when
Brandon Scott let her know just how personal he expected his
personal secretary to be.

Chance of a Lifetime by Joan Smith

Handsome John Balfour was number one on the Millionaire
Eligible Bachelor List of Kim Monk's roommate. But Kim loved
John for himself, not his wealth—how could she convince him
she was nothing like her friend?

Partners in Love by Jean Saunders

Robin Pollard's promise to be Luke Burgess' assistant seemed
like a terrible mistake. The rugged stranger not only wanted to
develop the wild Cornish landscape she loved, but it seemed he
had plans for Robin as well . . . plans she didn't
think she could resist.

Rain on the Wind by Elizabeth Hunter

Pippa had been too unhappy with her deceitful husband to ever
marry again. But Joel was determined to initiate her into the
delights of love she had missed the first time, and Pippa was
strangely vulnerable to this blond giant's slanted smile.

The Singing Stone by Rena McKay

Jordan Kyle seemed to be exactly the kind of man Jennifer's
mother had warned her against: a sun-bronzed maverick who
specialized in women on a two week holiday. But could it be that
he really was the tender man Jennifer thought she glimpsed
behind the glorious mask?